THIS BOOK BELONGS TO

_____
_____
_____
_____

Mandy

STORIES FOR GIRLS 1976

Printed and published by D. C. Thomson & Co., LTD., 185 Fleet Street, London, EC4A 2HS.

CAPTAIN JOHN BENNET and Don Davis were members of the British team which set out to climb the unconquered Mount Kachunga. They were only a few hundred yards from the summit—but they were in serious trouble!

NO USE... MUST REST!

NO, DON! IF YOU LIE DOWN, YOU'LL NEVER GET UP AGAIN!

The amazing

VALDA

A GIRL! HERE, NEAR THE SUMMIT OF KACHUNGA! BUT HOW?

MY NAME IS VALDA. I AM HERE TO HELP YOU. HOW I COME TO BE HERE IS NOT IMPORTANT, CAPTAIN BENNET.

YOU KNOW WHO I AM? I DON'T UNDERSTAND!

TAKE MY HAND, AND DO NOT SPEAK. I MUST CONCENTRATE!

Valda gripped the exhausted climbers by the hand, and a sudden surge of new strength and energy passed in a mysterious fashion to Bennet and Davis!

I FEEL WONDERFUL—FULL OF NEW STRENGTH. WE CAN TACKLE THE SUMMIT NOW!

Full of fresh hope, the men renewed the ascent of Kachunga.

WE'RE GOING TO DO IT—WE'RE ALMOST THERE!

VALDA SAID SHE ISN'T INTERESTED IN COMING TO THE TOP OF THE MOUNTAIN. JUST THINK, DON—WE'RE THE FIRST PEOPLE EVER TO STAND HERE!

LOOK! THERE'S SOME FAINT LETTERING ON THIS ROCK—AND A DATE! IT SEEMS WE'RE NOT THE FIRST TO CLIMB KACHUNGA—YET THERE'S NO RECORD OF ANY PREVIOUS EXPEDITION EVER REACHING THE SUMMIT!

V 1892

A sudden heavy mist descended on the mountain—

IT IS TIME WE RETURNED TO YOUR CAMP—FOLLOW ME.

IT'S UNCANNY HOW SHE CAN FIND THE WAY THROUGH THIS MIST.

But there was no welcome at the camp—

THERE'S BEEN A FIGHT— AND SCOTT AND PETERSON HAVE DISAPPEARED!

CAPTAIN— LOOK AT THIS!

LOOK AT THE SIZE OF THAT FOOTPRINT. AND...IT'S ALMOST HUMAN IN SHAPE. THESE STORIES ABOUT THE YETI, THE ABOMINABLE SNOWMAN—CAN THEY BE TRUE AFTER ALL?

KACHUNGA HIDES MANY SECRETS. COME—WE CAN DO NOTHING TO HELP YOUR FRIENDS HERE.

WE MUST SEEK HELP FROM THE MONKS AT THE MONASTERY OF THE SNOWS.

A MONASTERY—HIGH UP ON THE MOUNTAIN! BUT NO ONE KNOWS OF THE EXISTENCE OF THIS PLACE OR THESE PEOPLE. THIS IS INCREDIBLE!

Valda asked for an audience with Li-Chen, the Chief Priest.

I HAVE LISTENED TO YOUR STORY. WE WILL GLADLY GIVE YOU SHELTER, BUT WE CANNOT HELP YOU TO FIND YOUR FRIENDS—FOR WE DARE NOT DISTURB THE FORBIDDEN ONE.

I SEEK THE HELP OF THE ANCIENT MASTER, TO FIND OUR FRIENDS. MANY YEARS AGO, AID WAS GIVEN TO ONE WHO PROVED WORTHY— ONE WHO PASSED CERTAIN TESTS. I CLAIM THE RIGHT TO TAKE THE TESTS!

YOU KNOW OF THE THREE TESTS? THEN WE CANNOT REFUSE—BUT YOU MUST ALSO KNOW THAT THE PENALTY FOR FAILURE IS DEATH!

Out in the open courtyard—

STOP! IF THEY POUR THAT WATER OVER YOU, YOU'LL FREEZE TO DEATH—THE TEMPERATURE IS WELL BELOW ZERO! I CAN'T LET YOU DO IT, VALDA.

I SHALL COME TO NO HARM, CAPTAIN BENNET. THE MIND IS STRONGER THAN THE BODY!

THIS IS THE FIRST TEST—THE TOMB OF ICE!

SHE'S ENCASED IN SOLID ICE. SHE'LL DIE!

SHE MUST REMAIN IN THE ICE UNTIL ALL THE SAND HAS RUN THROUGH TO THE LOWER PART OF THE GLASS, THEN WE WILL RELEASE HER. IF SHE IS ALIVE, SHE HAS PASSED THE FIRST TEST!

TIME'S UP! THEY'RE GOING TO CUT HER FREE!

QUICKLY, MAN— GIVE ME THAT AXE!

WAIT!

THE ICE IS MELTING!

VALDA'S FREE— THE ICE HAS MELTED AWAY!

SHE SAID THAT THE MIND IS STRONGER THAN THE BODY—SOMEHOW SHE HAS CREATED ENOUGH HEAT TO DESTROY THE TOMB OF ICE!

OH, NO! SHE HAS COLLAPSED!

VALDA'S FACE IS CHANGING! SHE IS BEGINNING TO LOOK LIKE AN OLD WOMAN!

THE CRYSTAL OF LIFE...THE SUN... STAND BACK...

Valda feebly held aloft a crystal from the locket she wore round her neck. It caught the faint rays of the watery sun, and—

THE LIGHT FROM THE CRYSTAL IS DAZZLING —BUT VALDA IS STARING RIGHT AT IT! SHE SEEMS TO BE SOAKING UP THE RAYS!

I AM READY FOR THE SECOND TEST, LI-CHEN!

DID MY EYES DECEIVE ME? A MOMENT AGO SHE LOOKED VERY OLD! WHO IS VALDA—AND WHAT IS HER STRANGE SECRET?

Li-Chen led the way to a strangely-shaped rock pillar.

THIS IS THE PILLAR OF THE EAGLES. YOU MUST REACH THE SUMMIT— AND RETURN!

WHAT KIND OF ROCK IS THIS? IT'S AS SMOOTH AS GLASS— AND MY ICE AXE DOESN'T EVEN SCRATCH IT! IT'S IMPOSSIBLE TO CLIMB IT.

THE ONLY WAY TO REACH THE SUMMIT OF THE PILLAR IS TO JUMP ACROSS FROM UP THERE. LET US CLIMB THE SLOPE.

IT'S AN IMPOSSIBLE JUMP, VALDA. AND LOOK—THERE'S AN EAGLE'S NEST, WITH YOUNG BIRDS IN IT. THAT WOULD MEAN TROUBLE IF THE PARENTS RETURNED!

IT CAN BE DONE—AND I AM READY TO TRY IT.

THE CRYSTAL OF LIFE GIVES ME THE STRENGTH I SHALL NEED.

11

WHAT A LEAP! BUT IS SHE GOING TO MAKE IT?

SHE'S OVER—AND SHE'S KEPT HER BALANCE!

SHE'S SAFE FOR THE MOMENT—BUT LOOK! THE EAGLES ARE RETURNING TO THEIR NEST. THEY'LL THINK VALDA'S A DANGER TO THEIR CHICKS, AND ATTACK HER.

Then—

VALDA IS CALLING TO THE EAGLES—AND THEY'RE COMING DOWN TO HER!

NOW THE EAGLES ARE CARRYING VALDA BACK ACROSS THE GAP! IT'S AMAZING!

I REACHED THE SUMMIT AND RETURNED. I AM READY FOR THE FINAL TEST, LI-CHEN.

YOU MUST REACH THE FAR SHORE OF THIS UNDERGROUND LAKE—AND RETURN, BEFORE THE SAND RUNS OUT.

SHE'S GOING LIKE A TORPEDO!

But—

THE SAND RUNS OUT! VALDA HAS FAILED THE FINAL TEST!

THE LAKE IS WIDER NOW THAN IT WAS WHEN THE TEST WAS FIRST HELD. THE ACTION OF THE WATER THROUGHOUT THE YEARS HAS WORN AWAY THE BANKS.

CAN THERE BE TRUTH IN WHAT YOU SAY? I WILL HAVE THE LAKE MEASURED, AND COMPARE THE RESULTS WITH OUR OLD RECORDS.

The Ancient Master sprinkled herbs on a fire —

A mighty shadow loomed over Valda.

And, a few minutes later—

15

Valda returned to the monastery with the missing climbers—who could give Captain Bennet no account of their experiences. They remembered nothing!

GOODBYE, CAPTAIN BENNET. YOU HAVE CONQUERED THE SUMMIT OF KACHUNGA—I HOPE THE MOUNTAIN WILL BE LEFT IN PEACE FROM NOW ON.

THERE'S SOMETHING VERY STRANGE ABOUT VALDA. WHEN I GET BACK TO LONDON, I'LL TAKE THIS PHOTOGRAPH TO THE 'GLOBE'—MAYBE THEY CAN DIG UP SOME INFORMATION ABOUT HER.

But, six weeks later, in the office of the "Daily Globe"—

WE'VE DEVELOPED THAT FILM YOU GAVE US, JOCK—BUT I'M RATHER PUZZLED...

...WHERE IS THE MYSTERIOUS VALDA YOU'VE TOLD US SO MUCH ABOUT?

VALDA'S NOT ON THE PHOTOGRAPH! IT MUST BE A FREAK EFFECT OF THE LIGHT AGAINST THE SNOW...OR IS IT?

THE END

THAT'S MY BOY!

IT'S MISERABLE, HAVING TO DO THE SHOPPING EVERY SATURDAY. I BET GUY'S GONE OFF SWIMMING, JENNY.

JENNY **BATES** and Lucy Peters lived in the same street, and were always the best of friends—but the arrival of a new family, to the house between their homes, brought trouble. The Smiths had a teenage son called Guy, and both Lucy and Jenny decided to have him as a boy-friend! One Saturday morning—

PERHAPS HE'S GONE TO THE ROLLER RINK. HE'LL BE SPEEDING ROUND ON SKATES, WHILE WE TRUDGE OFF TO THE SUPERMARKET.

At the supermarket—

WELL, LUCY—I SUPPOSE WE'D BETTER MAKE A START. FRUIT AND VEGETABLE COUNTER FIRST, AND THEN—WHAT ARE YOU GRINNING AT?

I JUST SAW HIM—**GUY!** HE'S DOING THE SHOPPING —JUST LIKE US!

CAN I HELP YOU, GUY? I KNOW MY WAY ROUND THIS PLACE WITH MY EYES SHUT—

JUST GIVE **ME** YOUR LIST, GUY—I'LL FIND EVERYTHING FOR YOU!

IT'S ALL RIGHT, KIDS—**I'M** HELPING GUY. YOU CAN JUST RUN ALONG AND FILL YOUR OWN TROLLEYS.

I WAS LUCKY ENOUGH TO MEET JILL OUTSIDE—SHE'S DOING ALL MY SHOPPING FOR ME!

17

CAN YOU SEE A RED ICE-LOLLY? MUM SAYS I CAN HAVE ONE, BUT I CAN'T SEE ANY—

GET OUT OF MY WAY, YOU LITTLE PEST—BUZZ OFF!

I'LL HAVE TO STAND ON MY TROLLEY TO REACH THESE CARTONS.

NASTY LADY! I'LL FIX HER—

WHO PUSHED ME? HELP!

BUY THAT LITTLE BOY A BAG OF SWEETS, JENNY—HE DESERVES THEM!

ARE YOU ALL RIGHT, JILL? FORGIVE ME LAUGHING, BUT IT'S THE FUNNIEST THING I'VE SEEN FOR AGES!

I HATE YOU—I HATE EVERYONE!

HOW DARE YOU LET ALL THESE PEOPLE LAUGH AT ME? I'M GOING—AND YOU CAN DO YOUR OWN WRETCHED SHOPPING!

JILL, WAIT A MINUTE—

WELL, IT LOOKS LIKE SHE'S ABANDONED ME. WHAT DID I DO TO DESERVE THIS?

NEVER MIND, GUY. WE'LL HELP YOU TO FINISH YOUR SHOPPING.

WHAT'S COOKING?

"**H**AM salad?" Sue said to herself with a frown. "Anybody can make a ham salad. All you need is one of those plastic packs of vegetables from the supermarket and a few lettuce leaves. No, they don't want a ham salad. They want something special!

"I wonder?" she pursed her lips thoughtfully. "What can I make that's really special? Something that will impress Mr Mayhew right down to his hand-made New York shoes, and make him glow all over with pleasure and kind feelings in the direction of Dad?"

Sue stood in the bright, clean, empty kitchen of her home. She looked at the cooker. It was cold and uninspiring. The larder door was shut and did not give Sue any bright ideas. The electric kettle sat on the worktop doing nothing, and the fridge hummed aimlessly to itself.

"I suppose Mum told me to make a ham salad, because she thought it was the safest thing for ME to do! But I bet Dad would really prefer something special like a . . . like a . . ."

Sue Tilly's father was a design engineer, who did much of his work in a studio at the top of the house. Almost all his work came from a company based in New York, presided over by the great Washington Mayhew the Third. WM3, as he was called, was flying to England on one of his lightning visits — sudden, unexpected and probably explosive!

He had made it known that he wanted to see Sue's father as soon as he arrived, to check on the latest batch of design pro-

jects and models that Sue's father was working on.

So, with a stomach full of butterflies, George Tilly had driven to the airport with his wife, to welcome the big man to England. It was a longish drive to and from the airport, so Sue had all afternoon to prepare a meal before her parents arrived home with their trans-Atlantic bombshell in the early evening.

The idea was to soften up the temperamental Mr Mayhew with a nice meal, then to invite him up to the studio to inspect Mr Tilly's work.

George Tilly hoped desperately that the long journey would not have put his boss in too bad a temper.

Sue had been left to prepare the meal, and she was determined to do her best for her

dad. She felt sure that the high-powered executive had not jetted across the Atlantic expecting to come face to face with a supermarket salad!

It was up to Sue to soothe the man. Sue knew from films on TV that big business people spent fortunes on lavish meals, filling themselves with tasty tit-bits.

"Mum's ham salad won't keep the mighty Mr Mayhew mellow," she mused. "But what will?

"The cookery book!" Suddenly Sue was opening and shutting drawers in the work cabinet. Not there. A quick scamper across the living-room to the bookcase, and she found it.

"Loads of things in here," Sue thought, whirring through the pages with her thumb as she strolled back to the kitchen. She put the book on the table and began to browse.

"All I've got to do now is to decide what recipe to do, go out and buy the stuff, cook it and serve it up.

"Hors d'oeuvres . . . mmm . . . no need to bother with them. Only bits and pieces and very fiddly. Can't really call them a meal."

Sue rustled a few more pages.

"Soups. French onion . . . no, he might not like onion. Cold Borsch. No, better have something hot. In any case, it takes over three hours . . . Argentinian pumpkin . . . yuk! I think I'll miss out the soup. I'll concentrate on something really fantastic for the main course.

"Yes, that's it! Steak! All Americans love steak, and it's easy to cook. It's very dear though . . ."

Sue looked at the money Mum had left for her. "Just as I thought. Ham salad money. I'll have to think again," she sighed, picking up the book once more.

"Chicken. It's cheaper, and I could make a casserole. That sounds better.

"One three-pound chicken, two tablespoons butter, two tablespoons olive oil, twelve small onions . . . how small is a small onion, I wonder?

"What's this? Cut the chicken up into pieces! Yeogh! I don't think I could do that. Better find something else to do. Anyway, we had chicken the other day, and who wants chicken all the time?

"Chinese sweet and sour pork! Woweee! Now that really is something different! I can just imagine serving that up. Mum and Dad would fall off their chairs with surprise, and I bet it'd be a real eye-opener for old misery Mayhew. The recipe doesn't look too long, so that means it must be simple to do . . ."

Sue bent close and began reading.

"Oh, dear. It needs soy sauce and we haven't got any. Ginger root. We haven't got any of that either and I bet they won't have any in the shops down the road. So much for my rare delicacy of the mystic Orient!"

Sue pushed the cookery book to one side. It was not helping her to make up her mind at all. It was just making it harder, and time was slipping by while she read about impossible things like veal and partridge pie, lobster Americaine and a cake with a name like an Austrian hiccup called Kugelhupf.

"I must make my mind up to cook something that I KNOW I can cook."

So Sue ran through her repertoire of fried eggs and bacon, lemon and meringue pie from last Thursday's school cookery lesson, Irish stew and shepherd's pie. She did a very good Irish stew. At least, Dad always said so.

"That's what I'll do," Sue said out loud, with a voice firm with decision. "Irish stew, just the thing to fill the hungry, harassed traveller with nourishment and warmth."

The kitchen clock stared down at her from the wall.

"Oh, no. There isn't time to do that. I'd have to go to the butcher's and the green-grocer's . . . I'll have to find something quicker than that."

The cookery book was dragged out again. Pages were flopped backwards and forwards in despair.

"I must find something . . . boeuf strogonoff. I've heard of that but never had it. It's supposed to be something of a luxury. Let's have a look."

Sue looked. She could hardly believe her eyes.

"Nothing to it, and we've got almost everything in the larder, except for the beef, mushrooms and what's this . . . sour cream?"

Sue dashed to the shops. The mushrooms were easy. The sour cream was impossible! In fact, the woman in the dairy thought Sue was being cheeky, and told her not to come back! Everything they sold was fresh and they were proud of it.

Sue bought a carton of fresh cream, then dashed to the butcher, only to find him closing the shop.

"Sold right out of beef," he said. "You should have come this morning. There'll be more in tomorrow. But pork chops are nice. Do you want them before I put them away in the cold store?"

Sue bought pork chops.

"Good-bye, boeuf strogonoff and hello again, cookery book!"

Page two hundred and thirty-four offered the answer to Sue's prayer. Pork chops baked in cream — and it was fresh cream!

Sue started work, browning the chops in butter. She set the heat too high, the butter turned a nasty black colour and the chops stuck to the pan.

"Mum was right," Sue decided. "Ham salad coming up!"

Back to the shops quicker than ever. Shut!

"There's no chance of getting cheese, cucumber or anything else that would do for Mr Mayhew's salad," Sue groaned in total dismay.

But when one door closes another door opens, and this old saying applied to the shops in Sue's High Street. She was the very first customer through that newly opening door!

Sue beat her parents and the formidable Mr Mayhew home by several minutes. The table was laid, the plates warmed and dinner was ready to be served.

Washington Mayhew the Third came into the house like a whirlwind in human form.

"Where's the salad?" Mum demanded in a low voice. "And why have you put out fish knives and forks?"

"I couldn't get any ham," Sue whispered back desperately. "So I decided to buy fish and chips instead."

Mr Mayhew heard!

"Fish and chips!" he thundered. "Real ENGLISH fish and chips! Y'know, all the times I've been in this country of yours, I've never once been offered real English fish and chips. It's steak, steak, steak all the time. People seem to think we Americans don't like anything else!"

Mr Mayhew was well on the way to being in a good temper. He mellowed throughout the meal, and by the time he viewed George Tilly's work he was ready to promote him — on the spot — to the company's senior designer in Europe!

THE END

DOUBLE TROUBLE

SUSIE and Sheila Taylor were twins—similar in looks, but vastly different in nature. Susie was bright and breezy, while Sheila was quiet.

On the girls' twelfth birthday, one present was to provide some interesting surprises. . .

AUTOGRAPH ALBUMS! I'LL SOON FILL MINE, SHEILA—BUT I BET YOU'LL BE TOO SHY.

YES—I SUPPOSE I WILL, SUSIE. I'D NEVER HAVE THE NERVE TO ASK FOR SOMEBODY'S AUTOGRAPH.

Later that day—

STEVIE SPARKLE ☆ ☆ ☆ HERE TONIGHT!

OOH! STEVIE SPARKLE'S HERE! I'LL MAKE HIM MY FIRST AUTOGRAPH. NOW, LET ME THINK—

Later—

I MEANT TO BUY A NEW JACKET WITH MY BIRTHDAY MONEY—AND STEVIE SPARKLE LOVES FLASH CLOTHES. HE'S SURE TO NOTICE THIS SEQUINED JACKET, AND GIVE ME HIS AUTOGRAPH.

24

Meanwhile, Sheila was in a flower shop—

Special Tulip Bargain!

I'LL BUY THESE FOR MUM—SHE SAID THE HOUSE NEEDED BRIGHTENING UP.

Later that afternoon—

HE'LL NEVER NOTICE ME IN THIS CROWD—LOTS OF OTHER GIRLS ARE WEARING JACKETS LIKE MINE!

NEVER MIND, SUSIE. OOPS! I HOPE MUM'S FLOWERS DON'T GET CRUSHED.

WE HARDLY EVEN SAW HIM!

NEVER MIND, SUSIE—YOU LOOK FAB IN YOUR NEW JACKET.

I SAY, YOUNG LADY— MAY I HAVE A WORD WITH YOU?

IT'S STEVIE'S MANAGER —STEVIE NOTICED ME AFTER ALL!

YES?

NO, THE ONE WITH THE FLOWERS. STEVIE SPARKLE WOULD LIKE A WORD WITH YOU. WOULD YOU COME THIS WAY, PLEASE?

WHATEVER CAN HE WANT?

Backstage—

...SO YOU SEE, SHEILA—YOUR FLOWERS REMINDED ME THAT IT WAS MY MOTHER'S BIRTHDAY, AND ALL THE SHOPS ARE CLOSED. I WONDERED IF YOU WOULD LET ME BUY THEM FROM YOU?

YOU CAN HAVE THEM, STEVIE—IF YOU'LL SIGN MY AUTOGRAPH BOOK!

So—

Susie had a crafty plan—

26

I WONDERED IF STEVIE WOULD SIGN THIS—ER—FOR MY SISTER.

OKAY, SHEILA. YOU CAN WAIT IN HIS DRESSING ROOM, UNTIL HE FINISHES THE FINAL PART OF THE ACT.

When Stevie came in—

I THOUGHT YOU WOULDN'T MIND SIGNING MY SISTER'S BOOK.

OH, YES—SURE. YOU HAVE A TWIN, DON'T YOU? WELL, LET ME SEE...

WHERE HAVE YOU BEEN? LOOK WHAT STEVIE SPARKLE HANDED OUT FROM THE STAGE—COPIES OF HIS LATEST RECORD. YOU MISSED IT.

I DON'T MIND. WAIT UNTIL WE GET HOME—I'VE SOMETHING TO SHOW YOU AND MUM.

HE WAS EVER SO NICE, MUM!

I GOT HIS AUTOGRAPH TOO—LOOK!

SO—THAT'S WHERE YOU WENT AT THE BREAK!

YOU'VE GOT TO USE YOUR HEAD, THAT'S ALL.

LOOK! HE'S PUT **I'M TWO PEOPLE AS WELL**—AND HE'S SIGNED **PAUL SLATER**.

HE'S SIGNED HIS REAL NAME—HE SAW THROUGH YOUR TRICK! YOU GOT HIS AUTOGRAPH, SUSIE—BUT NO ONE WILL KNOW IT'S STEVIE SPARKLE! NEVER MIND—YOU CAN BORROW MY RECORD, ANY TIME YOU LIKE!

27

RUBBER STAMP

A rubber stamp of your own name is useful for marking all your school books, etc.
To make one you will need a cheap pencil rubber, about 1 inch by 1½ inches in size, a penknife—and a little patience!

Using a soft pencil, design your stamp on paper, putting a frame round your name, as above. The frame should be the same size as the rubber.

Fix the design FACE DOWN on the rubber, as shown. Now rub all over with a ballpoint pen.

Remove the paper, and you will find the design transferred to the rubber, in reverse. Cut carefully round the letters, removing the waste to a depth of about 1/16 inch. This will leave the letters and the frame standing out.

You can use the stamp as it is, but it is better to glue it to a handle made of hardboard and wood.

Make your own ink pad, too, using a shallow tin and a piece of felt.

I WISH WE COULD PRINT A PHOTOGRAPH OF THIS, JACK.

NEVER MIND—WE'LL MAKE DO WITH ONE OF YOUR LIGHTNING SKETCHES.

While Karen waited—

HI, TIM. HAVE YOU COME FOR TICKETS?

NOTHING SO LOWLY! MARLA LEE IS ARRIVING FOR A REHEARSAL IN THE HALL AT ANY MINUTE—AND SHE'S GOING TO GIVE ME AN INTERVIEW!

A little later—

EXCUSE ME, MISS LEE—I'M TIM GARSIDE, FROM THE WOODLEIGH CRUSADER—

SURE, HONEY—CAN YOU WAIT A MINUTE? DWIGHT, MY PIANO ISN'T HERE, AND THAT TRUCK DRIVER SAID HE'D LEAVE IT AT THE TOWN HALL. WHAT'LL I DO IF MY LUCKY PIANO'S GONE MISSING?

After the piano-pushers left—

TONIGHT CONCERT BY MARLA LEE THE GREAT AMERICAN JAZZ PIANIST

WONDER IF THERE ARE ANY TICKETS LEFT? I'LL JOIN THE QUEUE AND FIND OUT.

THE PIANO CAME FROM MY DADDY'S OLD SALOON IN NEW ORLEANS, AND IT ALWAYS TRAVELS WITH ME. BUT THIS MORNING, OUR BUS BURST A FANBELT, AND THIS TRUCK DRIVER SAID HE'D TAKE THE PIANO FOR US—

30

Then—

I TOLD THOSE FOOTBALLERS TO BE HERE BY NINE O'CLOCK TO COLLECT THE PIANO, AND THEY'RE NOWHERE IN SIGHT.

OH, DEAR! THEY LEFT A QUARTER OF AN HOUR AGO, MR WILLIAMS—WITH WHAT THEY **THOUGHT** WAS THEIR PIANO! I THINK WE'VE GOT TO DO SOME EXPLAINING TO MISS LEE.

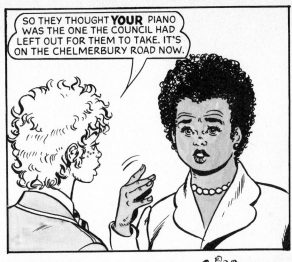

SO THEY THOUGHT **YOUR** PIANO WAS THE ONE THE COUNCIL HAD LEFT OUT FOR THEM TO TAKE. IT'S ON THE CHELMERBURY ROAD NOW.

Soon—

THAT'S THE ROAD THEY SAID THEY WOULD TAKE— ON THE LEFT.

THAT UPHILL TRACK—PUSHING A PIANO? YOUR BRITISH TEENAGERS ARE A TOUGH BUNCH!

FOUND YOU AT LAST. I'VE GOT NEWS, FOLKS—YOU'VE BEEN PUSHING THE WRONG PIANO! THAT ONE BELONGS TO MARLA LEE—AND HERE SHE IS TO RECLAIM IT.

GOSH! YOU MEAN WE'VE ACTUALLY BEEN PUSHING THE GREAT MARLA LEE'S LUCKY PIANO?

WOW! HERE COMES A SHEEP STAMPEDE—THEY'LL PUSH THE PIANO INTO THE DITCH!

SHOO! GET BACK—

IF YOU LOOK AN ANIMAL STRAIGHT IN THE EYE, IT OBEYS YOU. OH, DEAR—NOBODY'S TOLD **HIM** THAT!

The sheep halted behind the ram—

YOU SAVED MY LUCKY PIANO! ARE YOU OKAY, HONEY?

YES—BUT IF YOU DON'T MIND, I'LL JUST STAND WHILE THE BOYS HERD THE SHEEP ALONG TO THE FARMHOUSE!

OUCH!

When the sheep were safely out of the way—

HOW'S THAT, FOLKS? A SPECIAL PERFORMANCE BY MISS MARLA LEE, JUST FOR US!

SOMEHOW, KAREN, I THOUGHT WE'D HAVE TO HELP TO PUSH MISS LEE'S PIANO BACK TO WOODLEIGH!

CHEER UP, TIM. LOOK AT THIS FIVER—MARLA LEE GAVE IT TO ME, FOR OUR FUNDS!

That night—

THANK YOU, LADIES AND GENTLEMEN. AND NOW—A NEW NUMBER, PIANO PUSHER'S RAG AND IF YOU WANT TO HEAR ITS STORY— BUY THE WOODLEIGH CRUSADER NEXT FRIDAY!

SEE, TIM? FREE PUBLICITY— ALL ARRANGED BY YOUR STAR REPORTER!

THE END

Rent-A-Face *from Rosie*

JANE ROBSON owned a beauty salon where her young sister, Rosie, often helped. The girls started a special service —disguises for well-known people. One day, on the way to the salon—

LOOK, ROSIE—IT'S PRINCESS PATRICE FROM MONTICO. SHE'S HERE ON A PRIVATE VISIT.

IT DOESN'T LOOK VERY PRIVATE TO ME, JANE! STILL, I SUPPOSE SHE'S USED TO PUBLIC LIFE.

Later, in the salon—

THAT WAS SHIRLEY SHORE— YOU KNOW, THE SINGER. SHE WANTS US TO DO A DISGUISE FOR THIS EVENING.

I'M BOOKED THIS EVENING, BUT YOU CAN DO IT. YOU'VE MORE TALENT FOR DISGUISES THAN I HAVE —SHIRLEY LIKED THE LAST FACE YOU GAVE HER.

At the singer's home—

I'M SO GLAD THAT YOU'RE HERE, ROSIE. COME IN.

WHAT A PITY! YOU'VE MADE A FABULOUS JOB OF YOUR MAKE-UP—BUT I'LL HAVE TO CLEAN IT OFF, I'M AFRAID.

THE DISGUISE ISN'T FOR ME —IT'S FOR A FRIEND. SHE'S IN HERE.

PRINCESS PATRICE!

YOU MUST HELP THE PRINCESS, ROSIE. SHE'D LIKE TO GO OUT DINING AND DANCING, BUT SHE'LL BE PESTERED ALL EVENING IF PEOPLE RECOGNISE HER.

A LITTLE PRIVACY WOULD BE SO PLEASANT. I CAN HARDLY EVER RELAX AND ENJOY MYSELF, LIKE OTHER PEOPLE.

I'LL DO MY BEST TO MAKE IT POSSIBLE, PRINCESS.

I'LL BUILD UP YOUR NOSE—AND USE DARK SHADING TO CHANGE THE SHAPE OF YOUR FACE. YOU MUST BE CAREFUL NOT TO DISTURB THE MAKE-UP, THOUGH.

THEN YOU MUST STAY NEAR ME ALL EVENING, ROSIE.

So, that evening—

THE PRINCESS IS PLEASED WITH HER DISGUISE, SHIRLEY. BUT HOW AM I TO STAY NEAR HER?

THERE'S A TERRACE OUTSIDE THE RESTAURANT—YOU CAN KEEP WATCH FROM THERE, ROSIE.

OOH—IT ISN'T VERY WARM. HOW COSY THEY LOOK, IN THE CANDLELIGHT.

UGH! IT'S BEGINNING TO RAIN. I'M GOING IN AND I'LL HAVE TO AVOID THOSE SNOOTY WAITERS. IF THEY SEE ME, THE PRINCESS CAN'T EXPLAIN WITHOUT CONFESSING WHO SHE IS!

I'M GLAD IT'S DARK IN HERE—NOBODY'S NOTICED ME!

THIS IS FINE. IF THE PRINCESS NEEDS MY ASSISTANCE, I'LL BE CLOSE AT HAND—OR RATHER, AT FOOT!

Then—

THE LIGHTS! WHAT'S HAPPENED?

HOLD HER! SHE'S A THIEF!

The lights came on again.

WH-WHAT? IT'S FALLING APART!

JUST GLASS BEADS SET IN NOSE PUTTY—IT HASN'T QUITE DRIED, SYBIL.

THANK YOU, ROSIE. SYBIL AND HER ACCOMPLICE WERE LIKE PUTTY IN YOUR HANDS. NOW ALL IS WELL—

YES, PRINCESS. WE OUTSMARTED THEM—THEY'VE GOT TO FACE UP TO THAT!

THE END

ALMOST-HUMAN PUPPET

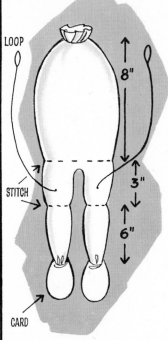

LOOP

8"

STITCH

3"

6"

CARD

You can have lots of fun with this wonderful puppet! Start like this, using part of the leg from an old pair of tights. Stitch across the centre and stuff with rolled-up paper. Tie at the top. Now, cut up from the bottom and stitch right round to form tubes for the legs. Stuff the top part of the legs and stitch across to make the knees. Stuff the lower parts of the legs with white paper, pushing them through holes in the card 'feet' and securing with a knot. Fasten threads to the knee as shown.

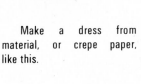

Make a dress from material, or crepe paper, like this.

Finish the dress like this, stitching up the sides and under the sleeves. Stitch on a big card bow and a tie at the neck. Slip it on your puppet and tie firmly round its middle with a sash.

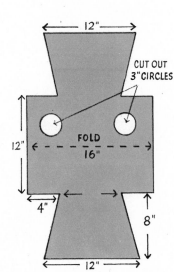

12"

CUT OUT 3" CIRCLES

FOLD

12" 16"

4"

8"

12"

You'll find your puppet can sing, dance, play an instrument—in fact, do almost anything you can!

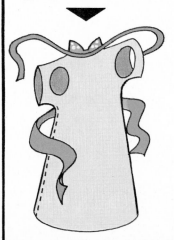

Now to bring your puppet to life. Tie it round your neck, put a table in front of the living-room curtains and poke your head and the puppet through the slit. Get someone to pin the curtains above and below your neck. Put your hands through the holes at the back of the dress and out of the sleeves, and your little fingers through the leg thread loops. Now you're ready to give your first show.

WHEN their parents died in the year 1840, the orphaned Shaws were turned out of their cottage. Rose, the eldest, vowed they would not be forced into the poorhouse, and she made a new home for the family— in a cave beneath the roots of a great oak tree, far out on Barsten Moor. The tree gave shelter and protection, and Rose named it—

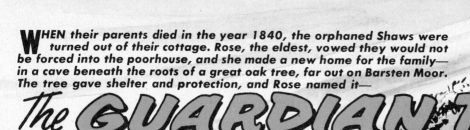

The GUARDIAN TREE

To make a little money for food, each day Rose gathered tufts of sheep wool left on bushes, and sold this in the village. One bleak day in early December—

IT'S GOING TO RAIN—MY BASKET IS ALMOST FULL OF WOOL, SO I'LL MAKE FOR HOME NOW AND SAVE MYSELF A SOAKING.

DRAT THE OLD WIND—NOW I CAN'T SEE CLEAR, FOR THE DUST IN MY EYES. WHO'S THAT COMING ON HORSEBACK?

INSOLENT BRAT! YOU—COME HERE, AND BE QUICK ABOUT IT.

IT'S THE SQUIRE'S SON! AND HE'S ANGRY.

It was Edward Beeston, the son and heir to the Squire of Barsten.

M-MORNING, MASTER EDWARD—MORNING, SIR. I GOT DUST IN MY EYES AND S-SO I DIDN'T SEE—

THAT IS FOR NOT MAKING YOUR CURTSEY WHEN I PASSED! YOUR PARENTS SHOULD HAVE TAUGHT YOU BETTER MANNERS.

Rose's eyes filled with tears of pain and anger—but the anger had to be hidden.

WHAT IS YOUR NAME, GIRL? WHERE DOES YOUR FATHER WORK? PERHAPS I SHALL ARRANGE FOR HIM TO LOSE HIS JOB.

MY NAME IS ROSE SHAW, AND MY FATHER IS DEAD. M-MY MOTHER TOO. I-I TAKE CARE OF MY YOUNGER BROTHERS AND SISTERS, M-MAKE A LITTLE MONEY BY DOING ODD JOBS.

I WAS FEARED HE WAS GOING TO STRIKE ME AGAIN, THE LOOK ON HIS FACE WAS SO UNPLEASANT.

I'LL WAIT A FEW MINUTES, THEN HAVE SOME SPORT.

HE'S GOING TO RUN ME DOWN! I MUST JUMP—

THE ROTTEN BEAST! I'VE LOST THE WOOL THAT TOOK ME SO LONG TO GATHER—THE WIND IS CATCHING IT.

ON YOUR FEET! RUN, RABBIT—RUN!

Half an hour passed—half an hour of fear for Rose, as she ran, stumbled and swerved.

HE'S LIKE A CAT WITH A MOUSE—AND THE MOUSE IS ME! HE'S GETTING HIS SPORT IN SEEING ME DODGE, LIKE A HUNTED ANIMAL.

OOH!

Rose tried to get up, but the pain beat her.

I-I CAN'T RUN ANY MORE, MASTER EDWARD. I'VE HURT MY BACK BADLY.

THEN LET THAT BE A LESSON TO YOU, ROSE SHAW. IN FUTURE, SHOW PROPER RESPECT TOWARDS YOUR BETTERS.

I CAN'T WALK—I CAN'T! THE PAIN IN MY BACK IS SO BAD, I'M NEAR TO FAINTING WITH IT.

I COULD DIE HERE OF COLD AND PAIN, AND WHO WOULD CARE FOR MY BROTHERS AND SISTERS THEN? IT WOULD BE THE POORHOUSE—THAT DREADFUL PLACE—FOR THEM. I MUST MOVE! I MUST GET HOME, FOR THEIR SAKES.

In the cave house, the younger Shaws were worried.

JOE! AND DANNY AND ANNIE. I'M—I'M HOME!

DANNY AND ME FOUND YOU LYING A LITTLE WAY OFF FROM HOME, AND CARRIED YOU TO THE CAVE. WHAT HAPPENED TO YOU, ROSE?

Rose said nothing of the Squire's son. She said that she had tripped and hurt her back.

WILL YOU NEED THE DOCTOR, ROSE? IS—IS YOUR BACK BROKEN?

NO, JOE. JUST A STRAINED MUSCLE, I THINK. I'D LIKE A CUP OF TEA. WOULD YOU AND DANNY SEE TO THAT, WHILE ANNIE HELPS ME GET INTO DRY CLOTHES?

OOH! HOW DID YOU GET THAT? DID SOMEBODY HIT YOU, ROSE?

NO! I-I CAUGHT MY ARM AGAINST A ROCK.

I MUSTN'T LET THE BOYS KNOW ABOUT EDWARD BEESTON. THEY'D WANT TO PAY HIM BACK—AND THAT WOULD ONLY BRING TROUBLE!

DON'T YOU WORRY ABOUT ANYTHING, ROSE. DANNY WILL HELP ME TO GATHER MORE WOOL—AND WE'LL DO THE COOKING, AND WAIT ON YOU LIKE YOU WERE A ROYAL PRINCESS!

I'LL SEE TO LITTLE LUCY, AND KEEP OUR HOUSE CLEAN.

I'VE GOT THE BOTTLE OF LINIMENT OUR MAM BOUGHT, WHEN DAD HURT HIS BACK. IT SOON PUT HIM RIGHT, AND IT'LL DO THE SAME FOR ME. ANNIE CAN RUB IT IN.

THE LONELY LAPWING

AT the beginning of March a pair of lapwings were flying back to their farmland breeding grounds. They travelled with a small flock of others —all the birds had spent the winter on some marshes much farther west.

They passed high over the village church where the rooks were working on their nests in the surrounding sycamores, then they began to drop towards an area of rough pasture, sloping down towards a lazy little river.

As they flew over the farm buildings, their long, sweet whistling calls drowned the songs of larks and thrushes.

" The pee-wees are back," said the cowman to the boy who was helping him, as he let the cows into the Barn field.

" Perhaps we'll find some eggs this year," said the boy hopefully.

" You can look all day and only stumble on them by chance," replied the cowman. " And a good thing, too! Pee-wees never did any harm! In fact, they do a power of good, living on grubs and snails and suchlike!"

He had barely spoken when there was a loud crack and a whistle of a different kind. One of the lapwings lurched in its flight. Its steady wing-beats became irregular and lop-sided, and it began to sink much more rapidly than the rest.

" Well!" exclaimed the cowman. " Some young hooligan's taken a shot at the birds with an air gun. He's winged the poor thing. He could have the law on him — these birds are protected nowadays."

The lapwing, who had been hit, was a hen called Eiyu. Despite the pain in her wing, she managed to keep going and landed in the area where she and her mate had nested the year before.

It was a cruel home-coming. Eiyu did not know what had happened to her. There had been a sudden, piercing sting, then, when she tried to fold her wings, the hurt one refused to obey, but trailed at her side.

The flock's first thoughts were for food after their long journey. The injured Eiyu found it hard to concentrate on the search for grubs and insects.

Willee, her mate, feeding close at hand, could not understand what she was fussing about.

After a while, the pain became dulled, but still Eiyu could not fold the wing into its proper place.

Once they had fed, the lapwings stayed motionless, resting on the ground and all facing the same way. This was the last time they would act as a community for several months. Later, the males flew out to establish their breeding territories. Willee lost no time in claiming a particular stretch for Eiyu and himself.

Suddenly, all the other males became potential enemies and thieves.

With his long crest fully erected and the sun striking green and purple lights from his glossy back, Willee flapped to and fro with challenging cries.

If another male dared to cross his territory below a certain height, an aerial battle took place at once. White breasts flashed and quite a few feathers floated down. Lost feathers were the only real injuries from these battles — that, and the injured pride of the loser!

As soon as he was sure that the others recognised and respected his rights, Willee proudly went to fetch Eiyu who, like the other hens, took no part in the skirmishing. To his surprise, she could only follow him in a series of fluttering hops. By now, her wounded wing had stiffened and was useless for flying.

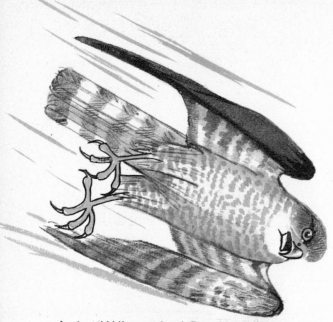

At last Willee realised Eiyu had been injured. He led her more slowly to the selected area. This was a stretch of rough grass scattered with clumps of rushes and a few thorn bushes.

In extra wet winters the little river, too lazy to flow much faster, let its waters spill over the valley. This kept the ground moist and made a good feeding place when the uplands were hard and dry. Eiyu could find all the food she needed without having to fly elsewhere. But she worried about not being able to fly when she wanted to, or when danger threatened.

But now the time had come to lay her eggs. She did not build a nest, but rounded out a little hollow in the grass with her breast and feet. In this, over a period of days, she laid four eggs. Their olive green and mottled brown colour blended wonderfully with their surroundings. They were extremely pointed at one end, so there was no chance that they would roll out of the shallow nest.

Once all the eggs were laid, Eiyu settled down to hatch them.

Eiyu did not worry about the damaged wing so much while sitting on her eggs. If any danger loomed, she flattened herself protectively over them, leaving Willee to dive to and fro with angry cries.

Willee was a conscientious husband, taking over duty when Eiyu slipped off the nest to stretch her legs and feed. At other times he kept strict watch, either by flapping to and fro like a policeman on the beat, or from a perch on a nearby fence post.

The worst moment of danger for Eiyu was from a girl riding a pony. The girl was watching the male lapwings wheeling overhead and did not think about where her pony's feet might fall. Shod with iron, they came closer and closer to the crouching bird. Just as it seemed she must be trampled into the ground, Eiyu jumped up, flapping her good wing and uttering a shrill cry.

The pony shot sideways

with a surprised snort and a buck for good measure. The girl, who was sitting carelessly, fell off into the grass. She got up to see the pony cantering away with reins and stirrups swinging. Never noticing the cause of her downfall, she ran angrily after her mount.

As the sounds died away, Eiyu settled back on her eggs.

At last the eggs hatched and the four chicks emerged. Eiyu had been eagerly awaiting the first signs of chipping. When the hard, smooth shells had broken down and she felt instead soft bodies stirring beneath her, she was delighted. Quickly she found Willee and told him.

Willee took the duties of fatherhood seriously, not only guarding the chicks, but helping with the feeding.

They did not stay long in the nest. They were soon on their feet, and running quite fast among the grass stems. This meant that they needed to be watched to make sure none of them strayed.

Eiyu was a very anxious and loving mother, and only felt her family was really safe when they were all together and cuddling under her feathers.

Now that the eggs had hatched, Eiyu became more aware again of her grounded state. Whenever she tried to fly with Willee she could only rise a few feet. A frenzied flapping of the good wing carried her sideways for a short distance before she flopped back to the ground. She no longer felt pain, but the pellet had shattered a vital bone.

Willee would fly round and round calling for a while before going off to feed on his own. So Eiyu gave up trying to fly. She could run very fast and cover a wide feeding area on her legs.

The chicks' worst enemies now were stoats and weasels on the ground and hawks from the sky.

One chick fell victim to a sparrow hawk. It came in a low swoop over the bushes. In a second it had struck and gone, carrying off the chick before Eiyu could even utter a warning cry.

After that she kept the other three close by her, until they had grown too big to be tackled by hawks. But this did not save them from the keen nose of a stoat, who came worming through the bottom of a thorn bush.

This time Eiyu saw him before he pounced, and acted in her instinctive way. She tricked him away from the chicks by running across his trail as if she were injured. It worked, but in this case the injury was not a fake one!

The stoat came after her while the chicks scattered. Although a small animal, he was savage enough to kill an adult lapwing if he got one on the ground. And Eiyu was now at his mercy, for she could not fly up at the crucial moment.

She cried out, though, and fortunately Willee was nearby. He came tumbling out of the sky like an acrobat. The stoat could not face the wing-flapping and screaming, and retired elsewhere.

The chicks grew rapidly, exchanging fluff for feathers. As they became able to look after themselves, the parents were able to relax. Soon their flight feathers were grown enough to let them become airborne. Once again Eiyu became upset about her uselessness as she saw her youngsters taking longer flights, encouraged by Willee.

While the young lapwings grew stronger and glossier, the adults began to moult. Grievances and squabbles were forgotten. They gathered once more in a sociable flock, feeding and bathing together.

This time was not so bad for Eiyu, except when the flock flew around, but it always came back to the same place where she could rejoin them.

As autumn drew near, the lapwings drew into an even closer flock and discussed their winter plans. One day they all rose up — all but Eiyu — and flew towards the west.

Eiyu knew that this time they were not coming back. She ran after them, flapping desperately to get off the ground only to fall back after a few yards. She cried out mournfully to Willee.

Willee heard and circled back. He flew round and round, urging her to try again. She tried and tried, but it was useless.

A battle went on in Willee's heart. He wanted to be with his mate, but instinct to go with the flock at that season was even stronger. At last he flew off after it, still calling to Eiyu.

When the last mournful note faded on the wind, Eiyu sank down, exhausted and all alone.

★   ★   ★   ★   ★

The will to survive was strong. Although she had been abandoned by both family and friends, Eiyu began feeding again as soon as she had recovered her strength. As she wandered around, searching for grubs and little snails, she continued to call, but no familiar voice answered.

The valley was very still now without the other birds. The solitary lapwing walked among the withering grass and plants like a lost waif.

Then one day Eiyu was lit up by hope when she heard the call of " pee-wee, pee-wee " overhead. A small flock of lapwings circled and then landed nearby. Although strangers, they were of her own kind and she greeted them eagerly. For a few days the valley became alive again, and Eiyu cheered up.

But it was not to be for long. This was only a resting spot on their journey. Soon they all took off, and Eiyu was alone again.

When frost hardened the ground, so that she could not push her bill through the crust, Eiyu fed along the muddy edge of the river. Here she was joined by a pair of herons who, making use of their long legs, waded nearly into the middle to fish. But they would fly off to roost in a distant oak, their powerful wing beats mocking the grounded lapwing.

Snow fell in January, and once again Eiyu had to depend upon the kindly river for food. Its waters were a dirty yellow against the white-covered banks, but there was enough feeding in the river to keep Eiyu from starving.

Hundreds of miles to the west, Willee and their children fed well on the mud flats of an estuary that never froze. With them were ducks, teal and wading birds. Some of these fell prey to the guns of wildfowlers who came creeping out in flat boats on nights of broken moonlight.

Eiyu had no more trouble from guns, but she nearly died one night in the jaws of a fox. Following

lapwing custom of feeding on long winter nights by moonlight, she was pecking along a shallow ditch, unaware of the fox hiding in some bracken.

The first thing she saw was the movement of the fronds as he sprang. Instinctively, she tried to take wing. The effort was enough to defeat the fox's first pounce. But Eiyu could not run fast enough to escape from him for long.

There was a thorn bush nearby, and she sped towards this as her only hope. Although unadapted for hopping on twigs, she fought and flapped her way up through it.

The fox's teeth almost closed on her tail feathers. He tried to climb after her, but the twigs were not thick enough to bear his weight and he tumbled back. By now Eiyu was well up into the

bush, and had the sense to stay there. She had to resist the temptation to use it as a launching pad. She would not have remained airborne for long.

The fox prowled round and round, glaring up from the shadows as if he would hypnotise her into falling out of the bush. At length hunger got the better of him, and he left to try his luck elsewhere.

On a mild day near the end of February, the first lark tried out his voice over the valley. Then a blackbird took over from the stormcock, who had shouted from the sycamores on Church Hill through the wildest weather.

Eiyu, who had become almost resigned to her lonely life, felt a fresh longing stir within her. She wandered restlessly about, calling plaintively.

Partridges were pairing with long, creaky love calls at dusk and early morning. Snipe darted in a crazy courtship, made even more odd by their trick of spreading their feathers to produce an eerie drumming sound as they dived through the twilight.

A little later, the hares were behaving just as crazily, the males sparring and even turning somersaults in their efforts to win mates.

All this activity made Eiyu feel lonelier than ever.

Then one day in March she heard faintly a well-known call.

"Pee-wee — pee-wee!"

With crest erect, Eiyu hopped and flopped eagerly in the direction of the call. Soon the sky was alive with wings and forms that looked black and white against the blue sky.

Down they came in ones and twos, putting out their pink feet to the grass and closing their wings as they landed.

Willee was among them, glossy and immaculate despite his long journey.

Joyfully Eiyu ran towards him. Then she stopped short with a sickening stab of dismay. Willee had a close companion, another hen, a young stranger he had met on that faraway estuary.

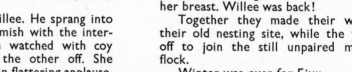

The young hen shook out her wings and started to preen her feathers, keeping a sharp eye on Willee. He recognised Eiyu at once, and started towards her, only to be stopped by a sharp cry from his new companion.

Realising she had an unexpected rival, the young hen flew up and landed a few yards away, calling to Willee to follow. Another cock promptly approached her.

This was too much for Willee. He sprang into the air and engaged in a skirmish with the interloping cock. The young hen watched with coy satisfaction while he drove the other off. She ducked her head up and down in flattering applause,

and brought him back to her side. But Willee's elation was spoilt by Eiyu's pleading calls. He was torn between his first love and the young hen.

Eiyu's heart was nearly broken. To meet her mate again, only to find him paired with another was worse than all the loneliness of the winter months!

"Yu-wee-weep-weep!" she mourned in the spring sunlight. "Twee-pee!"

Out of the blue another cock bird landed beside her. He was not the one Willee had just chased off, but a raffish old bird, the gay bachelor of the flock. Eiyu ignored his struttings and tail displays, and kept her own crest depressed.

But if the posturings raised no spark in Eiyu, they had an effect upon Willee!

Furious, he rushed upon the displaying cock, who promptly took off. The aerial battle was short and decisive, with the intruder in full flight before he had even lost a feather!

When Willee dropped down again, this time beside Eiyu, his fluffed out plumage made him look twice his normal size. He strutted to and fro between the hens, shaking out his wings and tail and jerking his head with bristling crest.

The young hen continued to applaud, but Eiyu turned her back, pretending she didn't care. Even with her drooping wing she managed to look aloof and dignified.

Eiyu's wiles won the day, for it finally made up Willee's mind for him. Now he focussed all his attentions upon her. Eiyu could not keep up the pretence for long, or conceal the joy swelling in her breast. Willee was back!

Together they made their way on foot to their old nesting site, while the young hen flew off to join the still unpaired members of the flock.

Winter was over for Eiyu.

MANDY'S CALENDAR FOR 1976

You can make an attractive calendar for **YOUR** *room, by cutting out the calendar pages throughout this book.*

Cut along the dotted lines which are marked on the pages for January/February, March/April and May/June.

Lay the pages neatly on top of each other—January/February on top, March/April second, and May/June third.

Now punch small holes through **ALL THREE** *pages, at the places marked by two small circles on the January/February page. You can use the sharp point of a pair of scissors to do this.*

Thread nine inches of wool through the holes, knot the ends, and your calendar is ready to hang up. You can turn the pages, so that the proper month is on top throughout 1976.

Mandy's Calendar

FOR 1976

JANUARY

S	—	4	11	18	25
M	—	5	12	19	26
Tu	—	6	13	20	27
W	—	7	14	21	28
Th	1	8	15	22	29
F	2	9	16	23	30
S	3	10	17	24	31

January's here again
With sleet and snow and hail and rain,
Frozen hands and frozen toes—
I hope you'll pardon my red nose!

But come on in, join Patch and me
Around the fire—there's toast for tea—
Hands and feet are warm at last,
Forgotten Winter's stormy blast.

We're roasting chestnuts by the score,
And Patch has gone to sleep once more,
But should tomorrow's dawn be white
He'll join us in our snowball fight!

February brings the snowdrops,
The first lambs frolic in the grass,
Daffodils in frilly bonnets
Nod 'Good-morning' as you pass.

Crocuses hold up their faces,
Drinking in the golden sun,
And down among the reeds and rushes
Preening feathers has begun.

This is the month for Cupid's arrow,
Loving hearts now intertwine,
I'll drop a hint—or boyfriend Tommy
May forget my Valentine!

FEBRUARY

S	1	8	15	22	29
M	2	9	16	23	—
Tu	3	10	17	24	—
W	4	11	18	25	—
Th	5	12	19	26	—
F	6	13	20	27	—
S	7	14	21	28	—

NOVEMBER

S	—	7	14	21	28
M	1	8	15	22	29
Tu	2	9	16	23	30
W	3	10	17	24	—
Th	4	11	18	25	—
F	5	12	19	26	—
S	6	13	20	27	—

Please to remember the fifth of November,
I hope that no one forgets
It's good without doubt, for YOU to be out,
But certainly not for your pets!

I'm locking up Patch and fixing the latch
So he's safely tucked-up and indoors—
When a rocket they light, it still gives me a fright
As into the darkness it soars!

DECEMBER

S	—	5	12	19	26
M	—	6	13	20	27
Tu	—	7	14	21	28
W	1	8	15	22	29
Th	2	9	16	23	30
F	3	10	17	24	31
S	4	11	18	25	—

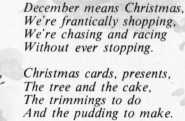

Merry Christmas

December means Christmas,
We're frantically shopping,
We're chasing and racing
Without ever stopping.

Christmas cards, presents,
The tree and the cake,
The trimmings to do
And the pudding to make.

When the great day is dawning
With everything done,
We'll be ready for Christmas,
And ready for fun!

Fay Fearless

FAY FEARLESS was a special agent with S O S, a secret government organisation which had its headquarters in Paragon Stores. One morning, Fay was summoned to a hidden office by Mr Felix, her superior in S O S.

NOBODY HERE. GOSH, WHAT'S THAT ON THE DESK? **UGH!** IT'S A GREAT HAIRY SPIDER!

IN YOU GO!

THIS OFFICE NEEDS DUSTING MORE OFTEN, MR FELIX! WAIT TILL YOU SEE WHAT I'VE FOUND—

A TARANTULA, MISS FEARLESS. AND YOU HANDLED IT VERY WELL!

Fay gave first-aid, and Michelle recovered.

As Michelle dried off in the hot sun, she explained her mission—

STOP—I'LL TELL YOU! IT'S MADE AT THE BELLEMONT PERFUMERY, JUST INLAND FROM HERE.

THANK YOU SO MUCH!

I WAS ONLY BLUFFING—BUT **HE** DIDN'T THINK SO!

MISS FEARLESS! WHERE ARE YOU GOING?

YOU'LL HAVE TO GUARD DR DUPONT AND WATCH THE PRISONER, MR FELIX—SO I'LL DROP IN AT THE PERFUMERY. I LOVE SCENT!

THIS IS THE PLACE. IT'S HARD TO IMAGINE DIRTY WORK AMONG ALL THOSE BEAUTIFUL ROSES. BUT I'LL GO CAREFULLY FROM NOW ON.

THAT TOUGH DOESN'T LOOK LIKE A FLOWER-FANCIER—HE'S MORE LIKE A GUARD! I'LL KEEP OUT OF SIGHT.

THERE'S JUST ROOM FOR ME TO CRAWL BETWEEN THE ROSE BUSHES! IT'S PRETTY SCRATCHY, THOUGH!

At tea-time—

WHY ISN'T TEA READY? WHY ISN'T MY DRESS WASHED AND IRONED?

BECAUSE MUM ISN'T HERE TO BE YOUR SLAVE, STELLA. HERE'S THE HOUSEWORK ROTA—FAIR SHARES FOR BOTH OF US.

WHAT? I'M SUPPOSED TO DO ALL **THAT** WORK?

YES! WHY SHOULD YOU WALTZ AROUND LIKE A LADY OF LEISURE, WHILE I'M STUCK AT THE KITCHEN SINK?

I AM GOING OUT. I SHALL HAVE SOMETHING TO EAT AT A RESTAURANT.

RIGHT. IF YOU GO ON STRIKE—SO DO I! I'M NOT LIFTING A FINGER, FROM NOW ON.

A short while later—

WE'LL SOON HAVE EVERYTHING PUT STRAIGHT, MOTHER!

THE NEW PEOPLE ARE ARRIVING NEXT DOOR. H'M—HE'S NOT BAD! JUST THE SORT OF BLOKE WHO COULD SOLVE MY PROBLEMS.

ER—HEM! WELCOME TO MARSTON. I CAN SEE THAT YOU'RE NOT SORTED OUT YET. WOULD YOU LIKE TO COME OVER FOR SUPPER, LATER THIS EVENING?

WHAT A CHARMING GIRL! MY SON AND I WILL BE DELIGHTED TO ACCEPT.

BABYFACE BOBBIE

BECAUSE she looked much younger than she really was, Policewoman Roberta Shaw was nicknamed "Baby-face Bobbie". Her youthful looks resulted in Bobbie being sent to Rowdown Academy as a "pupil"—and as a secret bodyguard for Karen Kronor, the daughter of the president of Translavia.

One day there was a school outing to historical Bladstock House, stately home of Lord Bladstock—

SCOTLAND YARD FEARS TRAPS HAVE BEEN LAID TO HARM KAREN KRONOR DURING THE SCHOOL OUTING TO BLADSTOCK HOUSE, CONSTABLE SHAW.

I'LL BE EXTRA ALERT, SUPERINTENDENT.

YOU MUST ALL BE ON YOUR BEST BEHAVIOUR, GIRLS.

YES, MISS PARR.

THIS IS JUST LIKE MY FATHER'S HUNTING LODGE IN TRANSLAVIA.

KAREN DOESN'T KNOW IT—BUT *SHE* IS THE ONE WHO MAY BE HUNTED HERE!

I COULD HAVE SWORN THAT STAG'S EYES MOVED!

I THOUGHT AS MUCH!

AAH! WHAT'S HAPPENING?

IT'S LORD BLADSTOCK!

YES, BY JOVE! I USE THIS STAG'S HEAD PEEP-HOLE FOR KEEPING AN EYE ON VISITORS. SOME OF THEM DO DAMAGE, Y'KNOW.

THIS IS A FINE START TO OUR VISIT, SHAW— EXPOSING HIS LORDSHIP TO RIDICULE, WHEN HE WAS ONLY WATCHING OUT FOR VANDALS SUCH AS YOU!

In the armoury—

ACHOO!

OBSERVE THESE FINE SPECIMENS OF MEDIAEVAL ARMOUR.

THERE'S SOMEBODY IN THAT ARMOUR— AND IT CAN'T BE LORD BLADSTOCK *THIS* TIME!

OOOH!

OUT YOU COME!

Later, in the dining hall—

Later, out in the grounds—

LORD BLADSTOCK HAS A FINE COLLECTION OF VINTAGE MOTOR CARS. SHAW—KEEP AWAY FROM THEM!

WHERE'S KAREN?

SHE PHONED FOR A TAXI. SHE'S GOING TO HER BANK IN TOWN, TO GET CASH TO PAY FOR THE DAMAGES.

GOSH! I MUST CATCH UP WITH HER!

STOP! GET OUT OF THAT CAR, SHAW!

HONK!

IT MUST BE AN OLD CROCKS' RALLY.

VROOM!

HONK!

Approaching the bank—

OH, HELP! I CAN'T STOP!

CRUMP!

AAH! OOH! WHAT'S HAPPENING?

THE SECRET LIFE OF HATEFUL HATTIE

HATTIE TAYLOR lived in Birch House Orphanage, in 1905. She was despised by the other girls, who gave her the nickname of "Hateful Hattie"—because she curried favour with the cruel staff, and was given special treatment. The girls did not realise that Hattie used her favoured position to help them.

A BOY FROM JARVEY'S EMPORIUM HAS DELIVERED THIS LETTER, MATRON.

THANK YOU, HATTIE. IT WILL BE CONFIRMATION OF THE ORDER MR JARVEY PLACED WITH ME YESTERDAY FOR HAND-STITCHED BED-LINEN.

The girls had to do sewing jobs to earn money for Matron, and her senior assistant, Miss Winters.

MR JARVEY HAS BROUGHT FORWARD THE DELIVERY DATE. THE WORK MUST BE COMPLETED BY THE FIFTH OF NOVEMBER.

B-BUT THAT'S ONLY EIGHT DAYS AWAY, MATRON! IT CAN'T BE DONE.

IT **WILL** BE DONE, HATTIE. FETCH MY CANE AND COME WITH ME.

THE GIRLS ARE IN FOR A BAD TIME OF IT NOW—EVEN WORSE THAN USUAL.

MATRON AND OLD WINTERS WILL WORK THE GIRLS UNTIL THEY DROP, AND THERE'S NOTHING I CAN DO TO STOP IT HAPPENING.

The day wore on—

WORK FASTER, YOU!

STAY AWAKE, YOU LAZY LITTLE BRAT!

IT SEEMS LIKE THIS DREADFUL DAY WILL NEVER END.

After midnight—

THERE WAS ONE GOOD THING ABOUT TODAY, GIRLS—HATTIE HAD TO WORK AS HARD AS **US**.

I THOUGHT THAT WOULD PLEASE THEM. BUT THERE ARE WORSE DAYS AHEAD, FOR ALL OF THEM.

After four days, not enough progress had been made.

WORK FASTER, YOU LAZY LOT. YOU'RE GETTING EXTRA FOOD—EARN IT!

THAT WAS MY IDEA. I PERSUADED MATRON IT WOULD GIVE THE GIRLS EXTRA ENERGY.

Then—

HATTIE, I WANT YOU TO GO ON AN ERRAND FOR ME.

IT'S NOT FAIR. HATTIE'S GETTING A REST FROM SEWING, AND SOME FRESH AIR. I HOPE SHE GETS RUN OVER BY A HORSE-BUS!

It was a very sad Hattie who returned to Birch House.

IT'S A CRUEL PLOT—ONLY MATRON COULD THINK UP ANYTHING AS NASTY. AND I HAD TO PLAY MY PART IN IT—THERE WAS NOTHING ELSE I COULD DO!

Later—

GIRLS, THIS IS MISS BARRINGTON, WHO IS TO BECOME ONE OF THE PATRONS OF BIRCH HOUSE.

MATRON MUST HAVE BEEN EXPECTING THE LADY—THAT EXPLAINS WHY OLD MISS WINTERS PUT HER CANE AWAY, AND WE'VE GOT A GOOD FIRE.

Miss Barrington spoke to the girls and praised their sewing.

BUT IT HAS TO BE FINISHED BY THE FIFTH, IF WE'RE TO EARN MONEY FOR THE ORPHANAGE. MR JARVEY IS INSISTENT.

I'M SURE THE GIRLS WON'T LET YOU DOWN, MATRON. BUT I BELIEVE IN REWARD FOR EFFORT—I HAVE AN IDEA.

IF THE WORK IS DONE IN TIME, I MYSELF WILL PROVIDE LOTS AND LOTS OF FIREWORKS THAT EVENING—AND A BONFIRE AND LOVELY EATS. I'LL COME AND JOIN IN THE FUN MYSELF.

THAT'S GREAT! TA, MISS!

THE GIRLS ARE HAPPY—AND THAT'S A CHANGE AT BIRCH HOUSE. BUT IT'LL BE ALL THE WORSE, LATER.

HATTIE, DEAR—MISS BARRINGTON AND I WILL TAKE TEA IN MY SITTING ROOM.

YES, MATRON. I'VE THE TRAY SET UP, ALL READY.

A few minutes later—

OH, WHAT A WONDERFUL JOKE! MY RIBS ACHE FROM LAUGHING.

A PRACTICAL JOKE, ENID— THE BRATS WILL WORK VERY, VERY HARD NOW.

THE IDEA CAME TO ME IN A FLASH, ENID— AND I KNEW, THAT WITH YOUR ACTING EXPERIENCE, YOU'D PLAY THE PART TO PERFECTION. SO I SENT HATTIE WITH MY NOTE, STRAIGHT AWAY.

HORRIBLE, CRUEL WOMEN— BOTH OF THEM!

MIND YOU DON'T LET THE CAT OUT OF THE BAG, HATTIE. I WANT TO SEE THEIR FACES WHEN THEY DON'T GET THEIR REWARD ON BONFIRE NIGHT.

HATTIE WON'T TELL. SHE'S A GOOD GIRL—SHE'LL ENJOY IT TOO.

Sick at heart, Hattie returned to the sewing room.

THE POOR THINGS. I FEEL SAD TO THINK OF THE CRUEL DISAPPOINTMENT THEY'LL GET.

HATTIE LOOKS MISERABLE. THAT'S BECAUSE SHE LIKES TO BE THE ONLY ONE TO GET TREATS—THE ROTTEN THING!

As Hattie passed Tilly—

OOPS! YOU WANT TO WATCH WHERE YOU'RE GOING, HATEFUL HATTIE.

HAVE YOU HURT YOURSELF, HATTIE?

MY—MY WRIST HURTS BADLY. I THINK I'VE SPRAINED IT.

It was a bad sprain. That night—

YOU SHOULD HAVE MANAGED IT SO SHE HURT A LEG, TILLY—THAT WRIST HAS GOT HER OFF SEWING. BUT AT LEAST IT HURTS HER A LOT, AND I'M GLAD!

YES, IT HURTS—BUT I'M NOT SAD, BECAUSE IT'S GIVEN ME AN IDEA.

Next day Hattie put her idea to Matron.

IT'S A VERY GOOD PLAN, HATTIE. YOU'RE A CLEVER GIRL.

I LIKE TO PLEASE YOU, MATRON— AND I WAS SO UPSET ABOUT MY BAD WRIST STOPPING ME SEWING FOR YOU.

OH, I HATE THIS ACT I HAVE TO PUT ON!

CAN YOU MANAGE ALONE, HATTIE? WITH MISS MOFFAT AND MISS MOLE HAVING FLU, I'VE NO STAFF TO HELP YOU.

IT WILL TAKE ME A WHILE BECAUSE OF MY WRIST, BUT I'LL HAVE IT MADE BY THE FIFTH OF NOVEMBER.

And in town on Guy Fawkes day—

OH, THANK YOU VERY MUCH, SIR! I **AM** DOING WELL.

HELP THE BIRCH HOUSE ORPHANS HAVE A HAPPY BONFIRE NIGHT

76

At the end of the afternoon—

MATRON WILL HAVE TO GET A GOOD BIT OF THE MONEY I'VE MADE, WORSE LUCK—BUT I'LL KEEP BACK THE REST TO BUY SECRET TREATS FOR THE GIRLS, TO EASE THEIR DISAPPOINTMENT.

I'LL BUY SWEETS AT THE SHOP AT THE END OF THE ALLEY, WHERE THINGS ARE CHEAPER. MAYBE SOME SPARKLERS, TOO.

Half-way down the alley—

COR, SHE'S A FIGHTER!

GIVE HER HEAD A HARD BANG. HURRY—THAT YELLIN' WILL BRING THE COPPERS.

The police came—but too late to save Hattie's money.

IT—IT'S GONE. ALL GONE—ALL THE MONEY.

I'M SORRY, LOVEY. THERE NOW, DON'T CRY. I'LL SEE YOU SAFE HOME, AND EXPLAIN WHAT HAPPENED.

Matron gave the policeman a real sob-story—

IT'LL BE A SAD BONFIRE NIGHT FOR THE GIRLS NOW, OFFICER. THERE JUST ISN'T THE MONEY TO BUY LUXURIES LIKE FIREWORKS.

MATRON'S HOPING HE'LL GIVE HER SOME MONEY—MONEY THAT SHE'LL KEEP TO HERSELF!

But—

NOT A PENNY FROM HIM! STILL, THE SEWING IS FINISHED AND THERE WILL BE FUN THIS EVENING, HATTIE—FOR SOME OF US, ANYWAY!

THERE'S A BONFIRE MADE. SHE'S GOING TO TAKE THE GIRLS OUTSIDE, AND THEN TELL THEM THAT THEY WERE FOOLED. SHE WANTS TO GLOAT OVER THEIR DISTRESS.

So, that night—

YOU MEAN—ALL THAT HARD WORK WAS FOR NOTHING? IT—IT AIN'T FAIR. IT AIN'T HUMAN TO DO THIS!

WE FOOLED YOU PROPERLY, YOU STUPID BRATS!

But at that moment—

HULLO, MATRON. I GOT UP A COLLECTION AT THE POLICE STATION. YOU'RE GOING TO HAVE FIREWORKS AFTER ALL.

AND TOFFEE APPLES, AND POTATOES BAKED IN THE BONFIRE, AND SAUSAGES.

It was a wonderful evening for the girls.

THE GIRLS ARE HAPPY—AND ONE DAY IT'LL ALWAYS BE LIKE THIS. UNTIL THEN, HATEFUL HATTIE WILL KEEP HER SECRET AND DO HER BEST FOR THEM!

The END

MARCH

S	—	7	14	21	28
M	1	8	15	22	29
Tu	2	9	16	23	30
W	3	10	17	24	31
Th	4	11	18	25	—
F	5	12	19	26	—
S	6	13	20	27	—

March, as mad as any hatter—
In like a lion—what's the matter?
Mother is dashing everywhere—
It must be spring is in the air.

Brandishing broom and wielding mop,
Will Mum's spring-fever never stop?
'Mandy!' she shouts, 'can't you get cracking?
That carpet on the line needs whacking!'

April's with us once again
With welcome sun and showery rain,
Her rainbow spans the grassy hills,
Her arms are filled with daffodils.

Pale primroses in hedgerow shade,
Shy violets in a woodland glade,
Happiness spreads far and wide—
It's April and it's Eastertide!

As into the blue the skylark soars,
Isn't it great to be outdoors?
I'll call for Joan this April day,
Then it's over the hills and far away!

APRIL

S	—	4	11	18	25
M	—	5	12	19	26
Tu	—	6	13	20	27
W	—	7	14	21	28
Th	1	8	15	22	29
F	2	9	16	23	30
S	3	10	17	24	—

SEPTEMBER

S	—	5	12	19	26
M	—	6	13	20	27
Tu	—	7	14	21	28
W	1	8	15	22	29
Th	2	9	16	23	30
F	3	10	17	24	—
S	4	11	18	25	—

September dandelion clocks
Are floating on the breeze,
Impatient swallows on the wires
Will soon fly overseas.

Blackberries festoon the lanes,
Patch loves them, so do I—
We ate so many of them once,
Mum couldn't make her pie!

Tommy loves September,
And can you guess the reason?
He welcomes it with outstretched arms—
For it's the football season!

OCTOBER

S	—	3	10	17	24	31
M	—	4	11	18	25	—
Tu	—	5	12	19	26	—
W	—	6	13	20	27	—
Th	—	7	14	21	28	—
F	1	8	15	22	29	—
S	2	9	16	23	30	—

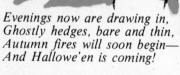

Evenings now are drawing in,
Ghostly hedges, bare and thin,
Autumn fires will soon begin—
And Hallowe'en is coming!

Squirrels scuttle to and fro
Rabbits snuggle down below,
Even Patch—he seems to know
Hallowe'en is coming!

In the dark, cats' eyes shine green—
Hark—was that a distant scream?
Did you say WITCHES have been seen?
Yes—Hallowe'en is coming!

Misfortune Manor

JANE MANSON looked about the hall of the Fortune Manor Hotel and decided that washing down the walls and paintwork had effected a slight improvement.

"Looks a bit less gloomy," Jane informed Tatters, the Mansons' dog, for want of a better audience. "But what's needed now is a paint job. A sunny yellow for the walls, and white for the doors and skirting boards. Right?" Tatters briskly wagged his tail. "Trouble is that paint costs money — and, as usual, we're broke."

She looked reflectively at the dog. "Wonder what I'd get if I put you up for sale? Your pedigree's O K — pure Old English Sheepdog — and you're affectionate and good with kids. On the debit side, you're completely scatty, and decidedly dim."

"He is not!" Jane's young brother Johnny came into the hall, and his cherubic face flushed red with indignation. "He's a smashing dog — aren't you, Tatters?"

Tatters lolloped to Johnny, tongue lolling. He reared up, planted his front paws on Johnny's shoulders and licked the boy's face with loving enthusiasm. Johnny staggered backwards, sat down with a thump and unsuccessfully tried to prevent Tatters from sitting down on him.

"Dead scatty," Jane insisted. "A real Manson. More of a Manson than I am, in fact."

"You can't help being sensible," Johnny said consolingly from the prone position Tatters'

weight had forced him into. "And we love you. Janey," he coaxed anxiously, "you wouldn't really sell him, would you?"

"Nobody would buy him," Jane said ruefully, then she smiled. "Anyway, I'd miss him — so that makes me just a bit scatty, too!" She looked towards the stairs and murmured under her breath. "And, talking of scatties, here come the two scattiest in the county."

"We're off now, Jane," said Miss Lottie Perkins. "On an errand of mercy."

"On an errand of mercy," echoed her sister, Miss Dottie. "Poor little Piggy," she added.

"Piggy?" Jane said in alarm. "You're going to buy a *pig?*"

The Misses Perkins collected stray or unwanted animals, and gave them a home. They'd been guests at the hotel for many years, and the Mansons had inherited them, along with the hotel, from Mr Manson's great-aunt, Miss Fortune. Under the terms of Miss Fortune's will, the Misses Perkins had to be allowed to stay at the hotel as long as they pleased, and the small amount they paid for their keep could not be increased.

The Mansons had also inherited the hotel staff. Lizzie Tucker was a cook and general help, whose actions were ruled by the portents she read in the cards and the tea-leaves. Her husband, Fred, was a most unhandy handyman.

"Is it a teeny-weeny pig?" Jane asked hopefully. "Just a piglet?"

"Oh, no," Miss Lottie said, beaming. "It's a dear old sow! This farmer wishes to be rid of her because she has developed some funny little habits."

"Funny little habits," Jane echoed hollowly. "Like what?"

"She thinks she is a dog," Miss Lottie said. "But now, we really must go."

Jane started off upstairs, muttering about scatty ladies and scatty pigs who thought themselves dogs, and met up with her sister Sam — short for Samantha.

"I'm off, Janey," Sam said sunnily. "Won't be back until tonight — I'm doing that Vitamex ad today." Sam was a model.

"Right," Jane said. "How much will the Vitamex ad pay?"

"Nothing," Sam said serenely. "At least, not in money. I'm taking payment in vitamin pills. Vitamex — they give you energy."

"We've got loads of *that*," Jane said, outraged. "It's the money we're short of. Honestly, Sam! Payment in pills! That's — that's scatty!"

"Well, they're short of money, too, Janey," Sam said, unperturbed. "The agency making the ad, I mean. They've just started up, you see, and they're working on a shoe-string budget. I was sorry for them. I mean, they're young and ambitious, but dead short of lolly. They want to go places."

"Me, too!" Jane said, with feeling. "Like a

desert island. A tropical one where I could just lie around, all on my own."

As Jane continued upstairs, a tortured wailing assaulted her ears. She winced.

"Oh, gosh! Just listen to Hayley ill-treating that trombone." Hayley, Jane's younger sister, was given to enthusiasms. Her latest one was for teaching herself to play the trombone.

Then Jane spotted Fred Tucker, with a hammer in his hand, on the landing. "Fred," she groaned, "what are you doing with that hammer?" The last time he'd used one, Fred had fractured a water pipe.

"Dunno, really," Fred said, swinging the hammer. Jane dodged smartly out of range. "Just looking for something to hammer."

"Not today, Fred." Jane whipped the hammer away from him. "I've a job for you — peeling the spuds for dinner. Lizzie can't do them. The cards and the leaves warned her against using sharp-edged tools."

Fred went reluctantly downstairs, and Jane went on up to her father's studio.

Mr Manson, an artist, was painting his favourite subject — his wife. She was a beautiful woman and a very serene one, with an enviable capacity for ignoring any of the harsher realities of life — like shopkeepers expecting to be paid.

"We need money," Jane announced, closing the door behind her and perching on a stool.

"Why, Janey?" Mrs Manson said. "We don't have to pay rent now, and we get fruit and vegetables from the garden."

"There'll be rates to pay before long," Jane reminded her mother. "And we can't live on fruit and vegetables — we need meat sometimes. We'll need clothes, too. Johnny's growing, Hayley's growing and — strange to relate — so am I."

"Nothing strange about that," Mr Manson said, standing back from the easel to eye his work critically. "Growing is normal."

"It's a miracle where *I'm* concerned," Jane said with feeling. "All the worries I've got should stunt my growth!" Jane grinned, and went on talking. "Seriously, though, I want to get this dump done up a bit during my holiday, and that means buying paint."

She stood up. "Dad, pick out half a dozen of your paintings, please. I'm going to take them into town and see if I can flog them."

"I'm painting your mother," Mr Manson said plaintively. "If I stop now I'll lose the creative flow."

"Sacrifices are called for," Jane said firmly. "Anyway, I need Mum to drive me into Downbridge. We'll have to go in Aggie, because I've searched out some other bits and pieces to sell. Late Victoriana — it's in demand these days."

Half an hour later they were off, with Mrs Manson at the wheel of Aggie, the family car, and chugging along at the slow pace suited to her advanced years. Piled up on the back seat were six

of Mr Manson's paintings, two aspidistras in large china pots, a china washbowl and water-jug, and four vases.

It took them an hour to get to the market town of Downbridge, and having parked Aggie they went off in search of a likely market for Mr Manson's pictures.

"There," Jane said, gesturing towards a shop. "See, it sells paintings and pottery and that sort of thing. Leave the talking to me, Mum — especially if the owner is a woman. If it's a man, you can smile at him. That might help!"

The owner was a man in his forties — bearded and affectedly arty in dress.

"Yes?" he said languidly as Jane deposited the six paintings, in a folder, on to the counter.

"Good morning," Jane said, and whipped open the folder. "This is your lucky day. I've six water-colours for sale, all by the well-known London artist Ben Manson."

"I'm over-stocked on water-colours, and I've never heard of Ben Manson," the man said, looking bored. His eyes went to Mrs Manson, and his face brightened. She smiled.

"He is very good," she said with enthusiasm. "I'm Mrs Ma——"

"She's Mrs Masters," Jane said quickly.

"Jane, dear," Mrs Manson said, eyes widening. "Are you all right?"

"Fine," Jane said. "Smile again," she hissed under her breath. "Mrs Masters — my mother — is a collector of the works of Ben Manson. She thinks he's wonderful." Mrs Manson smiled radiantly. "But she's forced to part with these because of a temporary financial crisis."

"Oh, dear," the man said. "Bad?"

"Very," Jane said truthfully.

"But I don't let it get me down," Mrs Manson said, equally truthful.

"How brave," murmured the man, and looked entranced at Jane's mother again. "Well, now, I'll take a look at the paintings."

"They're good," Jane said, spreading them out for his inspection, and that was the truth, too. Ben Manson was a fine artist, but his was an overcrowded profession.

"Eighteen pounds!" Jane said gleefully when they were outside the shop. "Great!"

"Wonderful," her mother agreed. "Look, Janey — there's one of those posh grocery shops on the other side of the road. We'll celebrate. Canned oysters are very good, and your father adores them. Or perhaps smoked salmon and——"

"Best end of mutton, from the butcher's," Jane said firmly. "This money isn't made of elastic, Mum, and it's not for luxuries. But first, let's get the junk out of Aggie and find an antique shop."

They only netted four pounds there, but Jane was in high spirits as they took the road back to Fortune Manor — or Misfortune Manor, as she had named it at first sight.

"I'll buy paint in the village," she told her mother. "The hardware shop has a sale starting

82

tomorrow. Wouldn't it be great fun, Mum, if I could get the hotel looking really super and attract lots of guests?"

"Yes, dear," Mrs Manson said vaguely. "Janey, is it a right or a left turn now?"

"Right," Jane said patiently. "Left would take you head-on into one-way traffic." She glanced at her watch. "We've been gone the best part of three hours. Wonder if anything has happened while we were away?"

She wasn't left long in doubt. Johnny, hopping about in excitement, rushed to the front door as they got out of the car.

"We've got the pig," he called. "She's called Susannah. She's playing with Tatters in the big lounge. She's got black spots, Janey."

"A pig in the lounge?" Jane said indignantly. "Not blinking likely — there are limits!"

"And we've got lots and lots of guests," Johnny said, bright-eyed. "We've got *ten* of them, Janey. Miss Lottie and Miss Dottie brought five of them, and the others just comed."

"Came," Jane corrected him, but she looked excited. "Ten guests — wonders will never cease. Where are they?"

"Five in the lounge — and the others, who came on their own, are upstairs talking to Daddy. He's told them they can stay as long as they like. There's Leo, and Vince, and Bob, and Jimmy, and David."

"Oh, no!" Jane wailed. "Oh, no! Dad's artist friends — I might have known the word would spread that we'd got a hotel. They'll be broke, as usual. They're just after free board and lodging."

"Come and see the other guests — the ones Miss Lottie and Miss Dottie found," Johnny said, tugging at Jane's hand and pulling her towards the lounge. "They're gentlemen, Miss Lottie said. Come and see."

In the lounge Tatters and a very large sow were gambolling around the room, the sow snorting and Tatters barking hysterically. At ease on the settees, the "guests" were being served tea and sandwiches by Miss Lottie and Miss Dottie.

"Gentlemen of the road," Lizzie Tucker said, joining a dazed-looking Jane at the doorway. "Tramps! Lottie and Dottie collects 'em each summer, gives them a holiday here. It's sort of traditional, you might say. Miss——"

"Miss Fortune always let them," Jane finished up for her. "Oh, my goodness — how ever am I going to get rid of them?"

★ ★ ★

JANE spoke sternly to the large pig lying in front of the door of her father's studio. "Susannah — if you don't move, I'm going to take hold of your tail and twist the curl out of it."

"Oh, Janey — you can't!" Johnny rushed along the corridor, chubby face filled with reproach. "Pigs are supposed to have curly tails, and if you made Susannah's straight she'd be unhappy. She'd feel odd."

"She's odd now," Jane retorted and nudged the pig with her foot. "Move! Pigs shouldn't be kept as house pets. Move, I said!"

Susannah opened one eye, gazed at Jane, grunted contentedly and then rolled over on to her back. Johnny knelt down by her and fondly scratched her tummy.

"Lovely Susannah," he crooned. "You like to have your tummy scratched, don't you?" Susannah assented with another grunt.

Just then Tatters came rushing along the corridor. He licked at Susannah's face with enthusiasm, then settled down beside her.

"They're friends," Johnny said with satisfaction.

"And they're both in the way. I want to talk to Dad." Jane leaned over the trio and hammered on the door. "Dad! Dad, open up!"

"Why don't you just open the door and step over them?" Johnny asked reasonably.

"Because Dad's locked the door," Jane answered with equal logic. "Dad, if you don't open up I'm going on strike. I mean that. And you won't get anything to eat, because this is one of Lizzie's non-cooking days. The cards and the tea-leaves warned her not to play with fire."

Mr Manson enjoyed his food, and after a few moments the door opened. He smiled at Jane, but she hardened her heart and responded with a stern look.

"We've got to talk," she said, and closed the door behind her. "Oh, you're in here, too, Mum—hiding, the pair of you."

"I was working," Mr Manson said, going back to his easel. "Your mother is modelling for me."

"Look, we need guests," Jane continued. "Paying guests — not a bunch of layabouts, and we've ten of those." She began to count them off on her fingers and thumbs. "Leo, Vince, Jimmy, David and Bob — your artist friends, Dad. And Joe, Alfred, Sidney, Tom and Barney — the tramps! We can't afford them. They've all got to go."

"But I told Dad's friends they could stay," Mrs Manson said plaintively. "For as long as they want to. Poor things, they need a holiday."

"And they're broke," Mr Manson said, equally plaintively. "I mean, friends should help one another."

"I agree," Jane said. "But the helping is always on our side, Dad. You're a soft touch, and they know it."

"We'll soon be broke again, if they don't go," Jane insisted. "They've big appetites — food costs money and we can't afford to feed them. They'll stay here for ever, if you don't let me put my foot down, Dad. Let me tell them to pack their bags and get off back to London. Then, with them out of the way, I'll deal with those tramps."

"No." Mr Manson spoke firmly now. "It would hurt their feelings, Janey. They'll move on, in time, but I won't have them being told to go."

"Any luck?" Lizzie Tucker asked Jane some half an hour later. "Here, dear, have a cup of tea. You look like you need it."

"I do." Jane settled on a stool by the kitchen table and sighed deeply. "Dad won't kick the artist lot out, Lizzie. I argued and argued, but no go. He can be firm sometimes."

"He's being preyed upon," Lizzie said darkly. "That lot — eating three good meals a day, and always asking for second helpings."

"And those tramps," Jane gloomed. "Phew! How they pong! They've got appetites like horses, too. As if it wasn't bad enough having Miss Lottie and Miss Dottie collecting stray animals, without them collecting up stray tramps!" Jane sniffed the air. "Those tramps have been in here recently, haven't they?"

"No." Lizzie set down a cup of tea in front of Jane. "It's Susannah's dinner you can smell. It's cooking on the range."

"I wish Susannah was far, far away on some range," Jane said bitterly. "Preferably in America. Or being cooked in the range," she added. "The food problem is getting dead dodgy."

"Miss Lottie and Miss Dottie would never stand for Susannah being used for bacon," Lizzie said with a sigh. "I mean, that's why they bought her, to save her from getting slaughtered. Funny little ways, she's got."

"Like wanting to be a house pet and imagining she's a dog and trying to sleep in my bed at nights. She always picks on me. Very funny! Ha-ha," Jane said mirthlessly. "I'll settle her somehow — but first I've got to get rid of the guests without asking them to go."

"Short rations?" Lizzie suggested. "Nasty-tasting meals?"

"Out!" Jane replied. "They eat with us, and if we short-served them, Mum and Dad and the Misses Perkins would give up their share. Lizzie, maybe they're all superstitious. Could you read the leaves and the cards for them, see all sorts of awful things happening to them if they stay on?"

"Oh, no!" Lizzie sounded and looked shocked. "Doesn't do to mock the cards and the leaves. I've told you that before, dear. Could bring dreadful things down on our heads."

"We've already got 'em!" Jane drank her tea and stood up. "I'm off to have a word with Miss Lottie and Miss Dottie now."

The two elderly ladies were playing with their motley collection of dogs on the lawns, and insisted on Jane "shaking hands" with each dog before she was able to raise the matter of the tramps.

"They're lying about in the big lounge," Jane

told them. "Feet up, smoking, dropping ash all over the carpet. How about them doing some work? Like helping wash down the paintwork?"

"But it's their holiday," Miss Lottie boomed.

"Their holiday," Miss Dottie echoed, on a high piping note.

"We'll clear up after them," Miss Lottie beamed. "Don't you worry, dear."

"Don't you worry," Miss Dottie came in, on cue.

"Somebody has to worry," Jane said. She ran a hand distractedly through her hair. "Look, if real guests come along, they'd be put off — those tramps haven't bathed since the year dot. At least I can tell them to take a bath!"

Jane marched back into the house and into the lounge to face the tramps.

"*Take a bath!*" they said a few moments later in shocked chorus.

"That's right," Jane said coaxingly. "A nice hot bath. You know — water, soap — bath."

"I can't," Sidney said. "On account of my chest." He coughed loudly for a full minute to illustrate his point. "It's weak; I've got to be very careful I don't take a chill. Be the death of me, most like."

Jane looked at Barney. "Now, Barney, what have you got against bathing?"

He told her at length, and the others were equally voluble. Jane left, defeated, and went back to the kitchen to get on with the preparation of lunch.

"Cup of tea going?" her sister Hayley asked a few minutes later, coming into the kitchen. "I'm thirsty. Playing the trombone is very thirsty work."

"Help yourself, the pot's half full," Jane told her, and then, after some thought, "Hayley, you can practise your trombone in the lounge if you like."

"No thanks!" Hayley retorted, and held her nose. "Phew!" she said nasally.

"Then go and practise it outside the room Dad's friends are using as a studio," Jane coaxed. "Make as much noise as you like."

"Why?" Hayley demanded.

"As a favour to me," Jane replied.

"O K, then." Hayley finished off her cup of tea and went off upstairs, from whence the tortured trombone soon gave forth.

"I do hope Hayley's trombone practice didn't disturb your concentration this morning," Jane said hopefully at lunchtime.

"Was she playing?" asked David, seating himself at table and eyeing the cottage pie hungrily. He helped himself — liberally. "I didn't hear."

"Nor I," came a chorus from the others, and Jane's face fell.

"We were absorbed in our work," Vince said loftily. "Like true artists. Probably wouldn't notice if the place fell down about our ears."

"It might come to that," Jane murmured under her breath. "That or the bailiffs in." She grabbed the dish of cottage pie away from David, who was about to pass it to Vince. "I'll be mother!"

Jane did some thinking. And that night, by dint of baiting the trail with apples, Jane got Susannah into David's room. He was still sleeping, as the pig started to scramble up on to the bed.

Grinning, Jane slipped away. Tomorrow, she decided, it would be Vince's turn. Then Leo, then Jimmy, then Bob.

"It might drive them back to London," Jane murmured as she climbed into bed. "Sharing a bed with a huge, smelly pig is no fun at all."

Five minutes later, Susannah trotted back into Jane's room and, grunting with the effort, got herself up on Jane's bed. Jane found some more apples, lured Susannah back to David's room, and this time shut her in. Then she went back to her own room and closed the door.

Fifteen minutes later, both doors were off their hinges, and Susannah was back on Jane's bed.

"Blinking pig!" Jane seethed, settling well over on her side of the bed. "I'll have to think of something else."

The following night Jane borrowed Hayley's trombone and settled herself in a corridor by the guest rooms.

"If any of them complain, I'll say I'm set on teaching myself the trombone," Jane told herself. "And night-time is the only chance I get."

"I blew and blew," she told Lizzie early next morning. "Blew hard enough and loud enough to bring down the walls of Jericho — and none of them so much as stirred! I blew for hours, Lizzie! My lips are hurting, and I feel dead tired."

"You look it," Lizzie said sympathetically. She spooned sugar into Jane's cup of tea. "Plenty sugar — for energy, dear."

"If only Dad wasn't so kindhearted," Jane sighed. "That's the root of the trouble, really. That, and him being dead scatty."

"A lovely feller, though," Lizzie enthused.

"Miss Emily would have liked him. You know, in Miss Emily's time, we used to have entertainments of an evening. Poetry reading, and Miss Lottie on the violin, with Miss Dottie singing——"

That was when Jane's face broke into a broad, beaming smile.

"Thanks, Lizzie," she said.

"For what?" Lizzie asked. Jane explained — and Lizzie laughed until she almost choked.

"Jane has asked my sister and me to entertain the other guests this evening, Mr Manson," Miss Lottie said at breakfast-time. "I shall play my violin and Dottie will sing, and we are both going to recite little poems. Ones we've made up ourselves about our doggies and pussies. We're very excited! It will be such fun!"

"We'll be out," Vince said promptly. "We go out in the evening." Miss Lottie's face fell.

"They'll be in this evening," Mr Manson said, noticing the sisters' sad faces. His voice had its rare note of firmness in it. "Yes, they'll be in."

They were, too — Mr Manson was a big chap, and his friends knew that when it came to preventing people's feelings being hurt, he could be firm.

"Good grief!" Vince murmured to David halfway through Miss Lottie's scrapings on her violin, and Miss Dottie's off-key singing. "I can't take much more of this."

"We'll have to," David whispered back. "Or Ben will chuck us out. Chin up, boyo — we can survive one evening of it."

After the music came the poems, very twee ones about pretty kitties and darling doggies. The artists' eyes grew more and more glazed.

"More!" yelled Jane, clapping hard. "More!"

"Encore! Encore!" shouted the kindly Mansons, and Lizzie and her husband, Fred. "More!"

"Perhaps tomorrow?" Miss Lottie said, blushing with pleasure.

"Tomorrow?" echoed Miss Dottie, beaming.

"Every evening, if you like," Jane said. "Eh, Dad?"

"Of course, of course," Ben Manson said kindly. "It's been a grand evening, Miss Lottie and Miss Dottie."

"I'm off tomorrow," Vince whispered in David's ear. "This torture is too big a price to pay even for free board and lodging!"

By noon the next day, all Mr Manson's friends had made their various excuses and left. Jane saw them off and breathed a sigh of relief.

"Miss D and Miss L can entertain just the family, and you and Fred," she told Lizzie. "Until they lose interest."

"They will, very soon," Lizzie assured her. "It's only their work with the animals they're consistent about. That and the tramps getting a holiday here."

"And that should be solved soon, with a bit of luck," Jane said. "I have another idea, but I'll need Miss Dottie and Miss Lottie to help me again — without them knowing it, of course."

Next morning, Jane set to work on the Misses Perkins, putting over her idea cunningly.

"Not for now, of course," she said when she had put the idea to them. "But in readiness for when their lovely holiday with us is over. It's your duty, really, to try and give them a better life."

"It's a wonderful idea," Miss Lottie said, and clapped her hands delightedly. "Wonderful!"

"Wonderful!" Miss Dottie echoed, and clapped her hands, too.

"But make it a nice surprise," Jane suggested. "Don't breathe a word of it to them until it's all fixed up."

"So you'll all have jobs when you leave here, boys," Miss Lottie told the tramps two days later. "Farmer Wright has kindly agreed to let you help with the fruit-picking. He had to be persuaded, but we coaxed and coaxed and said we were sure you'd work hard. What was it he said, Dottie?"

"He said 'You bet they will,'" Miss Dottie replied. "Wasn't that nice of him, boys?"

"Ah, but I have to move on — today. Urgent family business — me old granny is on her last legs," said Sidney, making for the door fast. "Got the message this morning, when you were out. Only stayed on to say good-bye."

"I'll go with you, Sidney," Barney said. "You need a good mate alongside you."

They all went with him, and the Misses Perkins looked sad until Jane told them she'd heard of a litter of kittens in need of a home. They went off, full of excitement, to fetch them.

"That only leaves Susannah to sort out," Lizzie said with satisfaction. "Though, come to think of it, she hasn't been indoors lately—"

"Not since the concert," Jane said, grinning. "She sat out two violin solos and then slunk out, her tail all limp. She's not risking coming back."

Jane crossed her fingers and added, "I hope!"

The GIRL with the SMILE

MARY MILLER longed to train as a nurse, but she missed out on a lot of schooling and fell short of the educational requirements. So Mary became a maid in the Children's Ward of Marchester General Hospital. This way, she could be a part of hospital life—and she kept her eyes and ears open, taking in everything to do with nursing.

I'VE NEARLY FINISHED THE PAINTWORK. I LIKE TO KEEP THE WARD LOOKING NICE—MAYBE SEEING IT BRIGHT AND SHINING HELPS THE CHILDREN TO GET BETTER.

MARY, I'VE DRAWN A PICTURE OF YOU. COME AND SEE.

THAT'S GOOD, JANICE. GOODNESS, YOU *HAVE* GIVEN ME A BIG SMILE.

YES, COS YOU *ARE* SMILEY, MARY. YOU NEVER GET CROSS WHEN WE ACCIDENTALLY SPILL THINGS, AND MAKE A MESS FOR YOU TO CLEAR UP.

SISTER JOHNS IS GREAT TO WORK FOR. NO WONDER I SMILE—THESE LAST THREE MONTHS IN HER WARD HAVE BEEN THE HAPPIEST MONTHS OF MY LIFE.

YOU'RE NICE! AND I HEARD SISTER TELL THE STAFF NURSE THAT YOU'RE THE BEST WARD MAID IN THE HOSPITAL.

MARY! I UNDID TEDDY'S BANDAGE TO SEE IF HIS EAR WAS GETTING BETTER, AND I DON'T KNOW HOW TO PUT IN ON AGAIN. WILL YOU DO IT?

THE NURSES ARE BUSY. I COULD DO IT, WITHOUT THEM NOTICING.

Sister Johns had bandaged the teddy's ear to amuse Johnny.

MARY WON'T HURT YOU, TEDDY. SHE'S KIND.

I'VE WATCHED THE NURSES BANDAGING, AND THEN PRACTISED IT IN MY ROOM AT THE STAFF HOSTEL, USING A DOLL AS A PATIENT.

Mary soon had Teddy bandaged up.

THANK YOU, MARY!

I MADE QUITE A NEAT JOB—IT WOULD BE NICE IF I COULD BANDAGE REAL PATIENTS. NEVER MIND, THOUGH. I'VE CHEERED JOHNNY UP, AND THAT'S GOOD ENOUGH.

Mary finished cleaning the paintwork, then gave out the mid-morning drinks.

I'LL LEAVE JOYCE UNTIL LAST, BECAUSE SHE'LL NEED TO BE COAXED TO DRINK HER MILK. POOR THING—SHE'S HAVING A BAD TIME OF IT.

Twelve-year-old Joyce Barton had been admitted to the hospital after a road accident two weeks previously, when a lorry mounted the pavement. Joyce and her mother were the only casualties—and Mrs Barton died of her injuries. Joyce suffered a broken leg and concussion. She cried a lot, and not only with pain. Joyce and her mother had been very close, and the girl was grieving deeply.

TRY, JOYCE. THE MILK WILL HELP YOU TO GET STRONG. I'LL HOLD THE GLASS FOR YOU TO SIP FROM.

NO THANKS. MY—MY THROAT IS ALL TIGHT. I—I CAN'T SWALLOW.

THAT'S FINE, JOYCE. NOW ANOTHER SIP—

EVERYONE IS VERY KIND TO ME, BUT I LIKE MARY BEST. SHE'S SO QUIET AND GENTLE.

Joyce drank all the milk and fell asleep.

THE MILK AND THE SLEEP WILL DO HER GOOD. WELL DONE, MARY.

I'M SO SORRY FOR JOYCE, SISTER. SHE'S SUFFERING SO MUCH, WITH THE PAIN AND MISSING HER MOTHER.

HER MOTHER'S NAME WAS ROSE, AND IT DESCRIBED HER PERFECTLY. SHE WAS BEAUTIFUL AS A ROSE, MARY. NOT ONE OF THESE STIFF, ARTIFICIAL-LOOKING ROSES—THEY TELL ME SHE WAS SO CHEERFUL AND LIVELY.

AND NOW SHE'S GONE. POOR MR BARTON— HE MUST BE SUFFERING TOO.

YES INDEED! BUT HE'S A GRAND MAN—HE HIDES HIS PAIN FROM JOYCE, AND TRIES TO COMFORT HER WHEN HE VISITS.

I WISH I COULD HELP JOYCE MORE— AND HER DAD, TOO.

Next day, at lunchtime—

IT'S TOO MUCH BOTHER SWALLOWING, MARY. EVERYTHING IS TOO MUCH BOTHER.

EVEN GETTING WELL? DON'T YOU WANT TO GET HOME, JOYCE? YOUR LITTLE BROTHERS AND SISTERS MUST MISS YOU.

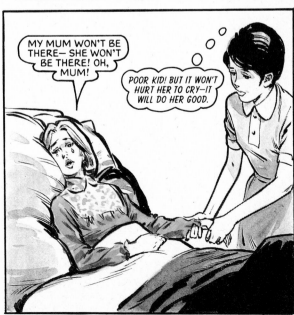

MY MUM WON'T BE THERE— SHE WON'T BE THERE! OH, MUM!

POOR KID! BUT IT WON'T HURT HER TO CRY—IT WILL DO HER GOOD.

HER DAD WILL BE HERE IN A COUPLE OF HOURS. THAT WILL HELP HER TO GET OVER IT—FOR TODAY AT LEAST.

POOR MAN! HE LOOKS WEARY, AND TERRIBLY SAD. THAT'S NOT HOW JOYCE WILL SEE HIM, THOUGH.

HE'S MANAGED IT AGAIN—HE'S PUT ON HIS CHEERFUL FACE, TO TRY AND CHEER JOYCE UP.

Then a thought struck Mary.

I WONDER IF THAT WOULD HELP? I FEEL IN MY HEART THAT IT WOULD, BUT I'M NOT SURE. I'LL THINK IT OVER BEFORE I DO ANYTHING.

Two days later, on Mary's day off—

I'LL JUST HAVE TIME TO DO IT, AND BE BACK FOR VISITING TIME.

HELLO, MARY! WHAT ARE YOU DOING HERE ON YOUR DAY OFF?

I JUST WANT TO GIVE SOMETHING TO MR BARTON. IS THAT ALL RIGHT, SISTER?

90

Sister gave permission—

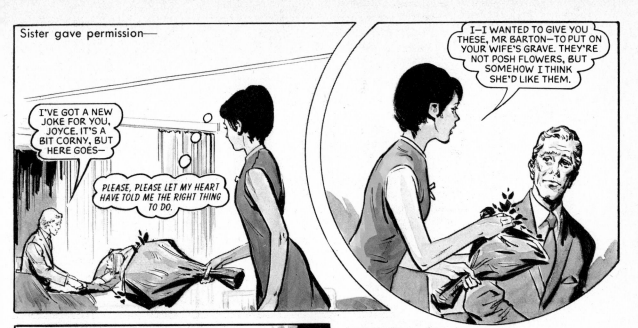

I'VE GOT A NEW JOKE FOR YOU, JOYCE. IT'S A BIT CORNY, BUT HERE GOES—

PLEASE, PLEASE LET MY HEART HAVE TOLD ME THE RIGHT THING TO DO.

I—I WANTED TO GIVE YOU THESE, MR BARTON—TO PUT ON YOUR WIFE'S GRAVE. THEY'RE NOT POSH FLOWERS, BUT SOMEHOW I THINK SHE'D LIKE THEM.

DOG ROSES, THEY'RE CALLED—BUT THAT'S NOT A GOOD NAME. MY GRANDAD CALLED THEM GOD'S ROSES. I WOULD HAVE SPENT MONEY ON THOSE STIFF ROSES, FROM THE SHOP, BUT SISTER SAID...

...WELL, SISTER SAID YOUR WIFE REMINDED HER OF A DIFFERENT SORT OF ROSE, AND THE WAY SHE SPOKE MADE ME THINK OF GOD'S ROSES. AND YOUR WIFE'S NAME BEING ROSE...

THAT—THAT'S A DEEP SCRATCH ON YOUR HAND, MARY. IT LOOKS SORE.

WELL, THE BEST ONES WERE NEAR THE TOP, AND I WANTED THE BEST. MRS BARTON MUST HAVE BEEN THE BEST, FOR YOU AND JOYCE TO LOVE HER SO.

Mary's words were too much for Mr Barton.
Tears trickled down his cheeks.

DAD—POOR DAD! YOU'VE STILL
GOT ME, DAD! I'M WITH YOU!
DON'T CRY.

COME, MARY—WE'LL DRAW
THE BED SCREENS AND LEAVE
JOYCE TO COMFORT HER
FATHER.

IT'S WHAT I HOPED FOR—THAT
JOYCE WOULD FORGET HER
OWN MISERY AND TURN
COMFORTER.

MARY'S LOVELY WILD ROSES MADE DAD CRY! IT'S
MADE ME REALISE I WAS BEING SELFISH, NOT THINKING
ABOUT DAD MISSING MUM AS MUCH AS I DO.

Next morning—

I'M GOING TO GET WELL, AND
GO HOME AS SOON AS POSSIBLE,
MARY. EVERYONE WAS
COMFORTING ME, BUT I DIDN'T
START TO FEEL BETTER UNTIL
I WAS COMFORTING MY DAD.

MY HEART *DID*
GUIDE ME PROPERLY.

The skill of the doctors and nurses would mend Joyce's broken bones—but
it needed the girl with the smile to start the mending of her heart.

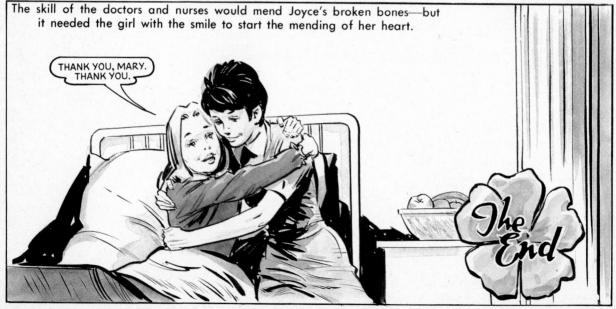

THANK YOU, MARY.
THANK YOU.

The
End

A Jumping Bean

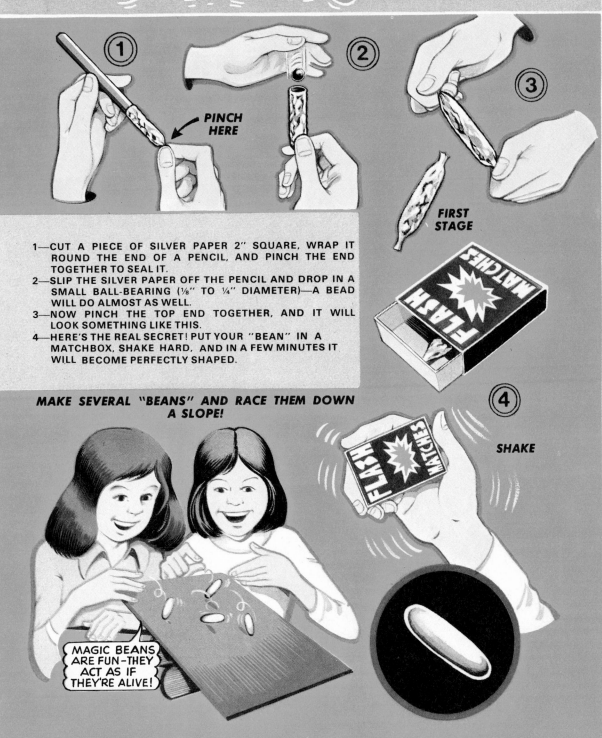

PINCH HERE

FIRST STAGE

1—CUT A PIECE OF SILVER PAPER 2" SQUARE, WRAP IT ROUND THE END OF A PENCIL, AND PINCH THE END TOGETHER TO SEAL IT.

2—SLIP THE SILVER PAPER OFF THE PENCIL AND DROP IN A SMALL BALL-BEARING (⅛" TO ¼" DIAMETER)—A BEAD WILL DO ALMOST AS WELL.

3—NOW PINCH THE TOP END TOGETHER, AND IT WILL LOOK SOMETHING LIKE THIS.

4—HERE'S THE REAL SECRET! PUT YOUR "BEAN" IN A MATCHBOX, SHAKE HARD, AND IN A FEW MINUTES IT WILL BECOME PERFECTLY SHAPED.

MAKE SEVERAL "BEANS" AND RACE THEM DOWN A SLOPE!

SHAKE

MAGIC BEANS ARE FUN—THEY ACT AS IF THEY'RE ALIVE!

LANKY LIZ

ELIZABETH knew she really didn't have time to do it, but she stood in front of her dressing-table mirror, tugging down the black school skirt so that it covered more of her thin legs. She stared at her reflection in dismay. She was not aware of her attractive face framed with short dark curls, and her sparkling blue eyes. All she saw was a tall "bean pole" with two spindly legs — legs made even skinnier by the dark grey school tights. No wonder everyone called her "Lanky Liz".

Liz had shot up rapidly after her twelfth birthday, outgrowing both her clothes and her classmates. Friends and visitors didn't mean to be unkind when they saw her, but they all uttered the same cry of, "My! Haven't you grown!"

Liz always felt like stamping with rage or weeping, but she was too well-mannered to do more than smile weakly.

Then she heard Mum's voice calling to her, "Hurry up, Liz. It's half-past eight. You'll be late."

After a final tug at her skirt she flew downstairs, gathered up her school things, and was on her way.

"At least I can run," she thought, as she tore along the road.

There were two things that Liz really enjoyed—acting, and sports of all kinds. She could be so carried away in either—so absorbed in a play or in the excitement of a game—that she forgot her tallness. Except when Sharon Fisher reminded her!

At the thought of Sharon Fisher a cloud seemed to settle over Liz, and she slowed down to a walk. By this time, however, she had arrived at the school entrance—and who should be just inside but Sharon Fisher herself, with a group of her cronies.

Liz was generally well liked but, for some reason, Sharon never lost an opportunity of taunting her.

Sharon was whispering something to them, leaning forward so that she didn't see Liz approaching. She was small and petite and, obviously conscious that she was pretty, she repeatedly tossed back her cascade of shining hair. She did this now and, as she raised her head, she caught sight of Liz.

"Liz needn't ever worry about being late. After all, if the gates are locked, she can always slip between the railings," she remarked in a loud voice.

Peals of laughter followed and Liz rushed past, her cheeks burning.

*   *   *   *   *

When the time for Physical Education came round, the short tunics they wore exposed Liz's thin legs to the full and Sharon was always ready with her jibes.

"Liz must be careful not to bend too sharply —her legs might snap," or "Don't jump too high

over the horse, Liz—you'll chip the ceiling."

It wasn't as if Sharon did well in the gym. She claimed that games bored her. And she showed no interest in the hockey and netball teams.

THE STAND-IN STANDS OUT!

BUT if Sharon kept in the background in the gym and on the sports field, she did just the opposite in the drama lessons. In these, she became the centre of attraction. She acted well, and everyone took it for granted she should get the leading female roles in any production.

Liz, too, welcomed any chance to act. Miss Thorne, the drama teacher, recognised her ability and usually gave her an important part to play. But, perhaps because she was tall, Liz found herself getting the men's roles and not the more glamorous ones which were always reserved for Sharon.

When the school presented a play for parents it was done in style, with impressive scenery and hired costumes, and Liz always felt a little twinge of envy when these arrived. For a historical play, wearing a man's costume, however colourful, can never be as thrilling as a beautiful dress!

In the drama lesson they were reading an Elizabethan play and no one had been allotted parts, as yet.

"Elizabeth," said Miss Thorne, "would you read the part of the Earl of Leicester. Sharon—you can try the Queen."

Sharon smirked and darted Liz a look of triumph. This put Liz off, and she read badly.

"Really, Elizabeth," Miss Thorne sighed. "You can do better than that. Perhaps, after all, I'll give that part to someone else. Anyway, let's stack the desks and try out the first scene."

The classroom became full of movement as the girls pushed the desks to either side to leave a space in the middle for the actors. Some of the desks were lifted on top of others, but the chairs were still clustered in the centre.

"Girls, could someone tall please lift a few of these chairs on top of the desks to make more room?" Miss Thorne requested.

"Liz can do it!" Sharon shouted gleefully.

Miss Thorne was growing impatient.

"Do hurry up, girls," she urged.

Liz lifted chair after chair on top of the desks, and eventually there was just room for one more. Sharon had one ready to pass to her but, instead of handing it over carefully, she suddenly threw it and Liz had to lean hurriedly sideways to catch it. She lost her balance, dropped the chair with a crash, fell against the other stacked furniture and brought the whole lot crashing down.

"Elizabeth Parkinson!" Miss Thorne's voice was shrill. "What do you think you are doing? I've never seen a longer, clumsier girl! Leave those chairs alone. Sit at the back out of the way!"

Liz crept to the rear of the room, her shoulders drooped, to make herself as small as possible—as small as she felt. She had to fight back the tears because, apart from the fact that her foot throbbed where a chair leg had stabbed into it, her feelings were hurt by Miss Thorne's remarks.

As the reading continued without her, Liz's misery increased. Being in the school play was what she lived for. She thought of little else, and it looked as though she had lost her chance now.

On the way home, her friends were sympathetic.

"That was rotten luck, Liz, but perhaps Miss Thorne will let you try the part again next time," Anne Marshall said kindly. But Liz knew there wasn't much chance of that.

As the days passed, the play gradually took shape. Another girl was doing quite well as the Earl of Leicester and Liz had been given a very small part. The drama lessons were an agony to her as she watched Sharon's self-satisfaction grow with each rehearsal.

Sharon took delight in making fun of Liz.

"Never mind, Liz. Miss Thorne might put in a dancing scene, and you could be the maypole!" she taunted.

But then Sharon went down with flu and was absent for a whole week. Rehearsals had to continue, so Miss Thorne asked Liz if she would read the part of Queen Elizabeth. Liz, of course, had so longed for such a part that she knew the words, the movements, everything—perfectly—so she could do it quite easily.

After the rehearsal the girls crowded round Liz. Congratulations were showered on her.

"You were terrific, Liz."

"You were much better than Sharon."

"Let's hope she has to have the rest of the term off."

"Oh, no!" protested Liz. "You mustn't say that, even if she is a bit spiteful sometimes."

Sharon didn't have to stay off school for long. She returned the following Monday, and immediately resumed as Queen Elizabeth. Her performance that day was not her best. She was pale and listless, and was forever blowing her nose.

Miss Thorne addressed them after rehearsal.

"With all this flu about," she informed them, "we must have understudies for the leading roles. Elizabeth, will you understudy Sharon?"

Liz was delighted!

"It's better than nothing," she thought.

Sharon glared at her.

"You needn't hope I shall be ill again, Lanky Liz," she snapped, "because I won't!"

COSTUME TROUBLES

THE day of the play grew closer, then the costumes arrived. They were superb, gorgeous Elizabethan costumes in rich shades of burgundy, gold, greens and blues, with ruffs and lace and decorated with sparkling stones.

But the Queen's dress was magnificent! It was stiff enough to stand on the floor without being hung up at all. It was as wide as a door, being strongly hooped and stiffened. Liz touched the gold and emerald brocade, and longed to try the dress on.

Sadly she walked away. Then she heard Miss Thorne calling.

"Elizabeth, would you go to the Music Room and wait for me? I have something to say to you."

Liz's heart began to thump. Oh, dear! What had she done now? Miss Thorne's face had been very stern. She dragged her steps to the Music Room and went inside to wait. Did Miss Thorne no longer want her in the play at all?

The door opened and Miss Thorne came in.

"Elizabeth," she started, "I am suddenly faced with a problem. As you know, the costumes for the play have arrived."

"Yes, Miss Thorne, and they're lovely."

"Yes, yes! But, you see, I am afraid the queen's dress on Sharon is—" she paused—" just impossible. Sharon is simply not tall enough, and we certainly cannot attempt to alter a hired dress! The queen must not be overshadowed by the other characters and that costume needs someone tall and stately. Sharon has tried the dress on and realises herself that her figure and height are just not suitable. You are her understudy and, with your—er—build, you will be just right for the dress. Will you take over as Queen Elizabeth from now on?"

Liz was almost too overcome to speak.

"Poor Sharon will be upset!" she said finally.

* * * * *

Liz's performance was outstanding and, dressed in the rich robes of the queen, for the first time that she could remember she was proud to be tall and to hold her head high. Congratulations poured in from parents, staff and girls.

And, although Sharon Fisher could not bring herself to congratulate her understudy, she never used the expression "Lanky Liz" again!

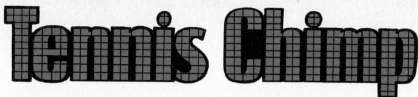
Tennis Chimp

CHERRY MARSDEN had an unusual pet—Julie, an intelligent chimp. Julie was a brilliant tennis player, and her acrobatic play usually proved too much for Cherry!

YOU'VE WON AGAIN, JULIE! YOU'RE TOO AGILE FOR ME!

At home—

IT'S A LETTER FROM AUNT BERTHA, JULIE. SHE'S INVITED US TO STAY WITH HER FOR A WEEK...AND SHE LIVES AT THE SEASIDE!

Later that week—

JULIE LOVES THE BEACH. SHE'S SPENT ALL MORNING BUILDING THAT CASTLE.

But—

OH, JULIE!

97

Julie forgave Gary, and they all became friends.

Mrs Griggs and her daughter Miriam were furious!

Cherry apologised, and then—

98

But—

JULIE! STOP THAT BALL—

AAGH!

WE ARE LEAVING. THAT MONSTER HAS RUINED OUR PICNIC.

WE'RE **VERY** SORRY. JULIE DIDN'T MEAN ANY HARM.

LEAVE MY DAUGHTER'S RACQUET ALONE. YOU WILL BREAK IT!

JULIE ONLY WANTS TO LOOK AT IT. SHE PLAYS TENNIS, YOU SEE.

DON'T BE SILLY! MIRIAM IS THE JUNIOR TENNIS CHAMPION OF THIS TOWN, AND I GO TO EVERY MATCH WITH HER. I'VE NEVER SEEN A CHIMP PLAYING TENNIS!

IF YOU'RE SO SURE JULIE CAN'T PLAY TENNIS, LET YOUR DAUGHTER PLAY A MATCH AGAINST HER. I BET JULIE WOULD WIN!

RUBBISH! THEY CAN PLAY A MATCH—AND IF MIRIAM CANNOT BEAT THAT ANIMAL, I WILL BUY EVERY ONE OF YOU A BEACH TOY.

So—

CAN JULIE REALLY PLAY TENNIS?

YES. WE OFTEN PLAY TOGETHER—AND I'LL KEEP HER RIGHT.

But—

THERE IS ONE CONDITION. YOU HAVE TO GO AWAY—THE CHIMP MUST PLAY ON HER OWN.

MIRIAM CAN'T LOSE NOW. IF THE CHIMP CAN PLAY AT ALL, IT WILL BE UNDER THE GIRL'S INSTRUCTION ONLY.

OK—I'LL GO.

THIS WILL BE A REAL TEST FOR JULIE, BUT SHE SEEMS CONFIDENT ENOUGH.

Julie started the match well.

WHAT A SERVE! THE CHIMP REALLY CAN PLAY TENNIS. I'LL HAVE TO DO SOMETHING, OR MIRIAM MAY LOSE!

GO ON, JULIE!

100

I'LL DAZZLE HER WITH MY MIRROR— ACCIDENTALLY, OF COURSE!

But Julie knew how to deal with tricks like that!

MY MIRROR!

Julie won the first game, and they changed ends.

WELL DONE, JULIE. KEEP IT UP!

OH! I'M SORRY. I DIDN'T SEE THE RACQUET.

GOOD! THE FIRST PART OF OUR SCHEME HAS WORKED—

When play resumed, Julie was not so successful.

MIRIAM DIDN'T MEAN TO BREAK YOUR RACQUET, JULIE. BUT, AS IT WAS HER FAULT, I'LL GET YOU ANOTHER.

THAT'S THE FIRST SET TO MIRIAM. IT SEEMS THAT JULIE DOESN'T PLAY VERY WELL WITHOUT CHERRY.

SKREEK!

GO BACK TO YOUR OWN SIDE OF THE COURT, IF YOU WANT THIS MATCH TO CONTINUE!

THAT'S MATCH POINT TO MIRIAM. WE CAN'T LOSE NOW!

THE CHIMP IS GOING! SHE'S GIVEN UP.

POOR JULIE. SHE TRIED HER BEST, AND NOW SHE'S UPSET BECAUSE SHE THINKS THAT SHE HAS DISAPPOINTED US.

Julie wasn't away for long!

IT'S JULIE! SHE'S COME BACK.

TENNIS CLUB

The match resumed with Miriam at match-point.

I'LL SERVE QUICKLY BEFORE SHE IS READY.

But Julie was able to scramble the ball back—

SHE'S RETURNED IT! BUT THIS IS AN EASY ONE TO DEAL WITH.

THERE! I'VE WON!

GREAT SHOT, JULIE!

Julie started playing well again—

—and reached match point.

HURRAY! JULIE'S WON. MRS GRIGGS WILL HAVE TO BUY US THE BUCKETS AND SPADES!

NO WONDER JULIE COULDN'T PLAY WITH THIS RACQUET. IT'S A CHILD'S TOY RACQUET, AND IT'S NOT STRONG ENOUGH TO PLAY REAL TENNIS. THAT'S WHY JULIE RAN AWAY. SHE MUST HAVE GONE BACK TO AUNT BERTHA'S, TO FETCH HER SPARE RACQUET!

The following day—

THE KIDS WILL HAVE A LOVELY HOLIDAY NOW—THANKS TO THE TENNIS CHIMP!

THE END

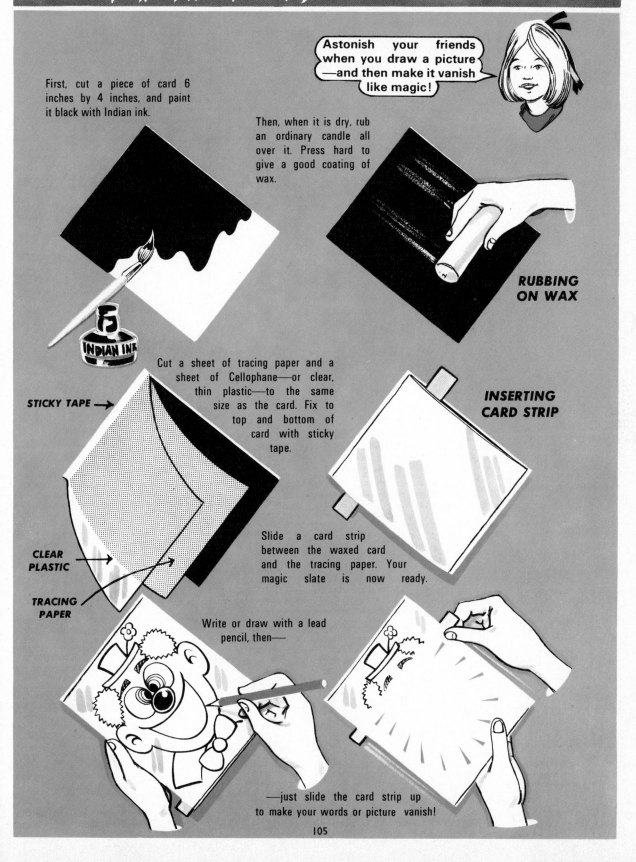

Astonish your friends when you draw a picture—and then make it vanish like magic!

First, cut a piece of card 6 inches by 4 inches, and paint it black with Indian ink.

Then, when it is dry, rub an ordinary candle all over it. Press hard to give a good coating of wax.

INDIAN INK

RUBBING ON WAX

Cut a sheet of tracing paper and a sheet of Cellophane—or clear, thin plastic—to the same size as the card. Fix to top and bottom of card with sticky tape.

STICKY TAPE →

INSERTING CARD STRIP

CLEAR PLASTIC

TRACING PAPER

Slide a card strip between the waxed card and the tracing paper. Your magic slate is now ready.

Write or draw with a lead pencil, then—

—just slide the card strip up to make your words or picture vanish!

105

LITTLE AUNTIE ANNIE

FIFTEEN-YEAR-OLD *Annie Johnson had taken on the task of looking after her ten orphaned nephews, who lived on a farm in Kentucky. The Johnson brothers—every one bigger and older than Annie—had been waited on hand and foot by their mother, and they all expected Annie to do the same.*

MRS O'HARA IS HOLDING HER SUMMER HOE-DOWN NEXT WEEK. IT'S SWELL, AUNTIE ANNIE—DANCING AND MUSIC AND LOADS OF FOOD! SHE'S SURE TO INVITE US ALL AGAIN THIS YEAR.

I'M SURPRISED THAT ANYONE INVITES YOU ANYWHERE! JUST LOOK AT YOUR DISGRACEFUL MANNERS—AND I DON'T BELIEVE ANY OF YOU BOTHERED TO WASH!

THAT'S MRS O'HARA'S FARM. SHE'S A WIDOW, BUT SHE KEEPS IT REAL SMART WITH JUST A FEW HIRED HANDS.

WELL—IF WE'RE GOING TO A PARTY, I'M GOING TO POLISH UP THE MANNERS AROUND HERE!

At dinner time—

NOW, BOYS—REMEMBER TO HOLD YOUR KNIVES AND FORKS PROPERLY, AND DON'T LEAN YOUR ELBOWS ON THE TABLE!

AW, AUNTIE ANNIE—WHAT'S ALL THIS FUSS ABOUT? MAW NEVER BOTHERED ABOUT HOW WE ATE.

WELL, **I'M** BOTHERING, SO JUST MIND WHAT YOU'RE DOING!

DON'T PUT YOUR KNIFE IN YOUR MOUTH, BARNEY!

OOOH!

At the end of the meal—

IT'S HOPELESS! NOTHING HAS ANY EFFECT ON THEM—NOT EVEN A ROLLING-PIN! I'LL HAVE TO THINK UP SOME OTHER WAY OF IMPROVING THEIR MANNERS.

Next day—

HARRY AND IAN, YOU TWO LAZY TWINS! YOU CAN COME INTO THE TOWN TO HELP ME DO THE SHOPPING.

OH—ER—WE'RE SORT OF BUSY, AUNTIE ANNIE!

But it was no use arguing with Auntie Annie!

WE'LL GO TO THE SUPERMARKET FIRST, HARRY. YOU CAN BOTH COME IN AND HELP ME.

WE MUST LOOK A PAIR OF CISSIES, TROTTING ROUND THE STORE LIKE THIS.

HEY—THERE'S JED SAMSON AND HIS BROTHER, SID. WE'LL NEVER HEAR THE END OF IT IF THEY SEE US. LET'S MOVE!

SALOON

THIS WAY—THEY AIN'T SEEN US!

AAAGH!

OH, DEAR! WHAT'S HAPPENED?

IT'S THOSE DISGRACEFUL JOHNSON RUFFIANS! THEY SHOULD BE LOCKED UP—TREATING A SUPERMARKET LIKE A SPEEDWAY TRACK! IT'S TIME THEY WERE TAUGHT TO BEHAVE!

AW, MRS O'HARA—WE'RE REAL SORRY! WE DIDN'T MEAN TO KNOCK YOU DOWN.

DON'T EVER DARE SET FOOT ON MY LAND AGAIN—YOU OR ANY OF YOUR IDLE, GOOD-FOR-NOTHING BROTHERS!

Later—

SO MRS O'HARA SAYS NONE OF US IS TO GO ON HER LAND AGAIN— THAT MEANS WE DON'T GET TO NO HOE-DOWN!

I'M SORRY, BOYS! IT WAS ALL AN ACCIDENT.

MY, AUNTIE ANNIE! THAT PIE SURE SMELLS GOOD!

THERE'S YOUR MEAL—MUTTON STEW AND BREAD! I'M NOT EATING WITH YOU AGAIN, UNTIL YOUR TABLE MANNERS IMPROVE. YOU'LL FIND ME ON THE VERANDAH IF YOU WANT ME!

WHAT'S GOT INTO AUNTIE ANNIE? SHE'S SURE MAKING A BIG FUSS ABOUT MANNERS.

HUH—MUTTON STEW! AND AUNTIE ANNIE HAS ROAST HAM AND CHERRY PIE! IT JUST DON'T SEEM RIGHT!

I HOPE THE BOYS ARE ENJOYING THEIR MEAL—*I* CERTAINLY AM! WHY—WHAT'S HAPPENING OVER THERE? IT LOOKS AS THOUGH MRS O'HARA'S BARN IS ON FIRE!

FIRE! ADAM, BARNEY, CHARLIE! FIRE!

WE MUST GET OVER THERE!

OK, AUNTIE ANNIE—WE GOT BOATS ON THE RIVER!

A few minutes later—

GET INTO A LINE AND PASS THE BUCKETS ALONG TO ONE ANOTHER. START OFF THE CHAIN IN THE KITCHEN.

THANK GOODNESS YOU'VE COME! I'VE PHONED FOR THE FIRE BRIGADE—BUT THE FLAMES ARE SPREADING SO FAST, THE HAY CROP WILL BE LOST BEFORE THEY ARRIVE.

Annie and the brothers worked desperately to control the fire.

KEEP GOING, BOYS! I THINK WE'RE WINNING!

Half an hour later—

STAND ASIDE, MA'AM—WE'LL FINISH OFF.

HOW CAN I THANK YOU FOR YOUR HELP? MOST OF THE HAY CROP IS SAVED—BUT I'D CERTAINLY HAVE LOST IT ALL, IF YOU JOHNSONS HADN'T APPEARED.

I HOPE YOU'LL ALL COME TO THE HOE-DOWN AS MY SPECIAL GUESTS! I GUESS I WAS OVER HASTY IN THE SUPERMARKET THIS MORNING.

THANKS A LOT, MRS O'HARA —WE'LL ALL BE THERE!

Next day—

WILL YOU EAT YOUR MEAL WITH US TODAY, AUNTIE ANNIE? WE'LL BEHAVE BETTER, AND TRY TO REMEMBER WHAT TO DO WITH THE KNIVES AND FORKS.

VERY WELL! WE'LL TRY IT TODAY AND SEE HOW IT GOES.

MY PLAN DIDN'T TAKE LONG TO WORK OUT. I RECKON IT WAS THE MUTTON STEW THAT CHANGED THEIR MINDS FOR THEM!

NO ONE STARTS UNTIL WE'RE ALL READY! HOLD YOUR KNIVES PROPERLY—AND DON'T FORGET TO SAY PLEASE AND THANK YOU!

A few days later—

THEY'RE ALL TRYING VERY HARD—I'M SURE THEY WON'T DISGRACE ME AT THE HOE-DOWN TOMORROW.

Next day—

HUH! ALL THAT HARD WORK GETTING THE BOYS TO USE KNIVES AND FORKS PROPERLY—AND HERE WE ARE EATING WITH OUR FINGERS AT A BARBECUE!

THE END

ONE JUMP FORWARD

ANNE trotted gaily up the road with a rising sense of excitement. At last she was about to ride over real show-type jumps and take the first step towards achieving her long cherished ambition to become a top show jumper. But, as she turned her pony into the tiny jumping paddock, she was aware of an unwelcome feeling of guilt.

Anne's elder sister, Esther, paid rent for the little field. Esther, with help from some admirers, had built, painted and erected the jumps, and she had forbidden Anne and her pony, Star, to enter the paddock.

Anne had been furious.

"You're mean," she had stormed. "How can I become a show-jumping ace when you won't let me practise over proper jumps ? When you were my age you jumped Star at dozens of shows and won lots of things."

"When I was your age," Esther had retorted with sisterly frankness, "I was a very good rider. You're not even an average rider—you're hopeless ! I won't have you using my paddock until your riding has improved. You'll only break my jumps and make a mess of things!

"I'll try to borrow some cavaletti, and you can practise over them on the grass behind the house."

"Cavaletti !" Anne groaned. "Back to beginner's work over those horrid poles ! They're so low that Star can step over them."

Anne worked hard to improve her riding. She read instructive books and tried to follow their advice. She scrutinised show-jumping programmes on television and noted the methods of the stars. She rode across the cavaletti until Star's hoofprints had worn a trench ! And still Esther deemed her sister incompetent to practise over her precious jumps !

Today, however, Esther was competing at a show.

"Covering herself with rosettes and glory, as usual," thought Anne sourly, as she turned Star towards the jumps.

Star bounced with joy, remembering the exciting Saturdays passed with Esther in a whirl of jumps, bright rosettes and rippling applause. He was bored by cavaletti. The wings of the coloured jumps stretched towards him, like the arms of welcoming friends, as he flew to meet them.

Star soared over the first jump with birdlike ease. Anne also soared, and only regained contact with the saddle by furious clutching at the reins. Star grunted as the bit struck the sensitive bars of his mouth. He threw up his head and rushed on. The second jump was a small, flimsy gate. With increased speed and raised head, Star misjudged it. There was a crash, a splintering sound, and the gate was borne to the ground.

"Oh, dear," thought Anne,

struggling to regain her stirrups, "whatever will Esther say?"

Star rushed on, clearing a triple bar with a light spring, which landed his still stirrupless rider heavily on the ground!

As a final boob, Anne allowed the reins to slip from her hands. She sat up and watched Star enjoying a wild lap of dishonour round the field—reins and stirrups flying, head and tail held high. Then, as he swerved through the open gate on to the road, there was a shrill shriek of brakes.

Anne began to cry. Now poor Star almost certainly lay dead or injured on the road.

There was no sign of Star on the road—only a scowling motorist driving noisily off the grass verge.

"Why don't you close the gates, if you insist on falling off? Your pony's gone home!" he shouted angrily as he drove away.

Star, calm and unhurt, was dozing in the rectory stableyard when Anne arrived. He turned his head and whinnied at her approach. Anne threw an arm round his neck.

"Oh, Star," she whispered. "Thank goodness you aren't hurt. It wasn't your fault that things went wrong today. I shall never be able to jump at any show—let alone become a star."

Sadly she led him to his field and watched him trot off—a beautiful bright bay pony with black points, and on his small, keen head a tiny star from which he got his name. Anne noted it all; the strong, short back, clean limbs, powerful quarters, sloping shoulder, and low elastic gait. Then she went into the house, found paper and pencil, and began to draw.

"At least," she thought, "I can control my pencil if not my horse." She drew Star, unhampered by tack or rider, galloping happily amongst his native hills.

Anne drew well. In a few light pencil strokes she portrayed the little pony and the magnitude of the mountains.

The door flew open and Esther, lithe and laughing, danced in. As usual she held a bright bouquet of rosettes in her long, graceful hands, and was followed by an admiring male.

The boy-friend was not known to Anne. Esther chose her admirers for their usefulness as well as looks. The gang which had helped to erect the jumps had now been given the brush-off!

Anne decided that the newcomer must be very talented

for he was not handsome or spectacularly dressed. He was tall, round-shouldered, much too thin, and sombrely dressed. His hairstyle was not remarkable, and his powerful spectacles were framed with wire. Anne noticed that he limped. Then she saw the camera held clumsily in his arms, and decided that this must be Len, the young art teacher of whom she had heard Esther speak. Len had made a super film of the jumping at a recent show. Doubtless Esther wanted a replay to discover why her mare had faulted at the water jump there.

Len smiled, and looked less plain.

"Hello," he said to Anne. "Drawing? May I see?" He studied the sketch in silence for a long, long time. Anne seized the opportunity to make a whispered confession to Esther about the broken gate. It seemed wise to deal with the matter while a third party was around.

"Are you going to be an artist when you grow up?" Len asked.

"I might have to be," Anne answered sadly, "if I can't make the grade as a show jumper—that's what I really want to be!"

"Why?" demanded Len abruptly.

"Because—because I love horses more than anything in the world," Anne replied, rather surprised by his tone.

"I love horses, too," said Len, "and I can't even ride! The horse world is extensive, you know. It needs all kinds of people, and talents. How old are you?"

"I'm nearly thirteen, and I haven't even made a start to my career," confessed Anne sadly.

"Well, you're not exactly middle-aged!" Len smiled. "Your riding might improve. Personally, I won't consider it a tragedy if you don't make the show-jumping grade. It seems to me there are more top-class show jumpers than really gifted equestrian artists around—and that sketch of yours is very good indeed!"

He smiled encouragingly, and followed Esther through the door.

Anne sat for a long time, thinking in the silent room. Then she raised her chin from her hands and smiled. Of course, she would try to be a show-jumping star with all her strength, but if she failed—well, being a world-famous horse artist might not be so absolutely terrible after all.

Thanks to the day's disastrous events, Anne was one jump forward in life!

MAY

S	2	9	16	23	30
M	3	10	17	24	31
Tu	4	11	18	25	—
W	5	12	19	26	—
Th	6	13	20	27	—
F	7	14	21	28	—
S	1	8	15	22	29	—

*Give three cheers for Maytime, Spring's come down to reign,
And swallows are homing to this land again,
Three cheers for the humming of furry-backed bees,
In orchards of pink and white blossoming trees.*

*Three cheers for the cuckoo—how welcome her call,
Her wandering voice casts a spell over all—
Three cheers for the maypole beribboned and gay
(D'you think they'll choose me to be Queen of the May?)*

JUNE

S	—	6	13	20	27
M	—	7	14	21	28
Tu	1	8	15	22	29
W	2	9	16	23	30
Th	3	10	17	24	—
F	4	11	18	25	—
S	5	12	19	26	—

*Mum says June is for lazing
And resting in the sun,
Or promenading in the park
When the busy day is done.*

*But not for me—not Mandy—
I'm mad on playing tennis,
I'm off for an evening foursome
With Tommy, Joan and Dennis!*

*Or else I'm in the local pool
Diving, floating, swimming—
I said Mum ought to join me,
It's very good for slimming!*

JULY

S	—	4	11	18	25
M	—	5	12	19	26
Tu	—	6	13	20	27
W	—	7	14	21	28
Th	1	8	15	22	29
F	2	9	16	23	30
S	3	10	17	24	31

Exams are all over and Sports Day is here,
July is my favourite month of the year.
I'm in for the high-jump and long-jump as well,
And in the track races I try to excel.

Last year Patch gatecrashed our hundred yards race,
He chased his friend Fifi all over the place!
So here's to July, it is sports time for me—
If I'm not competing, I watch on TV!

August means holidays, bask in the sun,
Complete relaxation for everyone.
Whether in Britain, or someplace like Spain,
Have a good time, want to go back again!

Climb up a mountain, surf off a shore,
Holidays bring you adventures galore.
Why am I dreaming? I feel such a fool—
My holiday's past, and tomorrow it's SCHOOL!

AUGUST

S	1	8	15	22	29
M	2	9	16	23	30
Tu	3	10	17	24	31
W	4	11	18	25	—
Th	5	12	19	26	—
F	6	13	20	27	—
S	7	14	21	28	—

A friend for Freda

FREDA BARTON'S father inherited a beautiful Elizabethan manor house. Freda loved her new home—but it was some distance from other houses, and she often felt lonely.

IT'S FUNNY! THERE'S NOBODY HERE—YET I FELT SURE SOMEONE WAS WATCHING ME.

OH! WHAT'S THAT I'VE KICKED UP?

IT'S A RING! IT'S BEAUTIFUL, AND IT LOOKS VERY OLD.

SO YOU'VE FOUND IT, FREDA—

WHO ARE YOU? WHERE DID YOU COME FROM?

I'M VICTORIA, BUT YOU CAN CALL ME VICKY—THAT'S WHAT MAMA AND PAPA CALLED ME, WHEN I WAS ALIVE.

ARE—ARE YOU A G-GHOST?

YES, BUT DON'T BE AFRAID. I'VE BEEN HERE FOR OVER ONE HUNDRED YEARS—YOU CAN SEE ME NOW, BECAUSE YOU ARE WEARING THAT RING.

YOU ARE THE FIRST ONE I HAVE BEEN ABLE TO TALK TO, FREDA—AND I NEED YOUR HELP. PLEASE—COME WITH ME, AND I WILL SHOW YOU SOMETHING.

IF YOU PUSH BACK THESE WEEDS, YOU'LL FIND A SLAB SET IN THE GROUND. YOU SHOULD BE ABLE TO LIFT IT.

YOU'VE DONE IT! NOW YOU WILL SEE THE SECRET ROOM WHERE I USED TO PLAY.

Freda ran back to the house for a torch, then led the way down the steps.

THIS IS SUPER, VICKY. IT MUST HAVE BEEN CLOSED UP FOR YEARS. WHAT WAS IT USED FOR?

AS A HIDING-PLACE, IN TIMES OF TROUBLE. THERE IS A PASSAGE BEHIND THAT DOOR—IT LEADS TO A CUPBOARD UNDER THE STAIRS IN THE HOUSE.

THE DOOR'S LOCKED. BUT I'LL ASK DAD TO OPEN UP THE PASSAGE, AND PUT A LIGHT IN HERE. THEN WE CAN PLAY TOGETHER, WITHOUT ANYONE KNOWING ABOUT YOU.

THAT WOULD BE LOVELY—BUT DON'T WORRY ABOUT ANYONE ELSE SEEING ME. ONLY *YOU* CAN DO THAT, WHEN YOU WEAR THE RING.

Freda told her parents about the room—

IT'S A BIG ROOM—AND WELL HIDDEN, TOO. FANCY YOU FINDING IT, FREDA.

CAN WE CLEAN IT UP, DAD—SO THAT I CAN USE IT AS A PLAY ROOM?

THAT'S THE PASSAGE OPENED UP. IT'S TOO LATE TO DO ANYTHING ELSE TONIGHT, FREDA. BUT TOMORROW IS SATURDAY— WE COULD SPEND THE WHOLE DAY CLEANING IT UP, IF YOU LIKE.

THAT WOULD BE GREAT, DAD.

The following day, after a lot of hard work—

WELL, THAT'S THE ROOM CLEANED. IT'S TIME YOU WENT TO BED NOW, FREDA.

OH! CAN I STAY—JUST FOR A MINUTE—TO HAVE A LAST LOOK ROUND?

Freda slipped the ring on—and Vicky appeared.

IT'S A CHEERFUL ROOM ONCE MORE. WE WILL HAVE SOME LOVELY TIMES HERE, TOGETHER.

YES, VICKY, WE WILL. CAN YOU COME BACK TO THE HOUSE JUST NOW? MUM AND DAD WILL BE WAITING FOR ME.

A few days later—

NOW THAT WE HAVE BEEN FRIENDS FOR SOME TIME, I WOULD LIKE TO ASK YOU TO HELP ME. BUT I'M AFRAID YOU WON'T LIKE TO DO IT, FREDA.

OF COURSE I'LL HELP YOU, VICKY. WHAT DO YOU WANT ME TO DO?

Vicky explained that, when she lived in the manor, her cousins lived in a house which could just be seen in the distance. One day, Vicky had an argument with her cousin. In a fit of temper, Vicky ran off with her cousin's ring, lost it—and from then on, the cousins hadn't spoken to one another. Then, a year later, Vicky died of consumption.

But now, Freda had found the ring—

MY COUSIN THOUGHT I WAS A THIEF—SHE DIDN'T BELIEVE I LOST HER RING. NOW I WOULD LIKE YOU TO HELP ME, BY RETURNING IT TO MY COUSIN'S FAMILY.

THAT'S THE HOUSE. MY COUSIN'S GRANDDAUGHTER LIVES THERE NOW, WITH HER CHILDREN. I'M SURE THEY WOULD LOVE TO HAVE SUCH A FAMILY HEIRLOOM RETURNED TO THEM—AND I WOULD BE FREE TO LEAVE THIS WORLD.

Vicky led Freda down into their secret room, and—

HERE IS A DIARY I KEPT. I'LL SHOW YOU WHERE TO FIND THE BIT ABOUT ME LOSING THE RING. YOU CAN SHOW IT TO THE PEOPLE, AND EXPLAIN HOW YOU FOUND THE RING—THAT WILL SURELY PROVE I WAS NO THIEF.

ALL RIGHT, VICKY. I'LL DO IT, IF IT WILL MAKE YOU HAPPY.

THIS IS AWFUL. I WANT TO HELP VICKY, AND MAKE HER HAPPY—BUT THEN I'LL LOSE HER AS A FRIEND. BUT MAYBE—MAYBE THE PEOPLE WON'T BELIEVE ME, AND VICKY CAN STAY WITH ME FOR EVER!

EXCUSE ME, BUT I THINK THIS RING BELONGS TO YOU. I'M FREDA BARTON AND I LIVE IN THE HOUSE OVER THERE—I FOUND THE RING IN OUR GARDEN.

BUT I HAVEN'T LOST A RING. WHAT MAKES YOU THINK IT IS MINE?

But when she saw the diary, Mrs Buxton became quite excited.

I REMEMBER MY GRANDMOTHER TELLING ME THIS STORY, WHEN I WAS QUITE SMALL. HOW AMAZING YOU SHOULD FIND THE RING—AND YOUR FAMILY MUST BE DISTANT RELATIVES OF OURS.

And when Mrs Buxton introduced Freda to her children—

MARION, ROBERT—MEET YOUR NEWLY-FOUND COUSIN, FREDA BARTON.

WHY, MARION LOOKS EXACTLY LIKE VICKY! WHAT A FANTASTIC FAMILY RESEMBLANCE!

Later—

YOU WON'T BE LONELY NOW. THANK YOU, FREDA—AND GOODBYE.

THE END

PAT'S CATS

PAT WHISKER worked at Pussy Willow Cat Kennels. One day, Lady Smythe-Jones brought in a prize-winning Siamese cat—

FENELLA IS **VERY** WELL-BRED. I DON'T WANT HER PICKING UP BAD MANNERS FROM ANY **COMMON** CATS!

VERY WELL, MADAM!

THE CUSTOMER IS ALWAYS RIGHT—EVEN THOUGH SHE'S A SILLY OLD SNOB!

OH, FENELLA—YOU'RE TEARING YOUR RIBBON!

Pat's cats came in to say "hello".

※ ??!!?? ※

WHAT A WAY TO TALK, FENELLA! YOU OUGHT TO BE ASHAMED OF YOURSELF!

At dinner-time—

REALLY, FENELLA—I'VE NEVER SEEN SUCH AWFUL MANNERS!

MILK

STOP FIGHTING AT ONCE, FENELLA! YOU'RE A RUFFIAN.

HERE'S YOUR ORDER, PAT.

A. HADDOCK FISHMONGER

DROP THAT FISH AT ONCE, FENELLA!

OW! YOU LITTLE SAVAGE!

At long last it was time for Fenella to go home, and—

WHAT YOUR MISTRESS WILL SAY, I DO NOT KNOW. WE'VE NEVER HAD SUCH A BADLY BEHAVED CAT BEFORE!

WHAT AWFUL-LOOKING CREATURES. I DO HOPE THEY HAVEN'T PASSED ON ANY OF THEIR BAD MANNERS TO DEAR LITTLE FENELLA!

?

!

THE SLAVE GIRLS

SORRY, GIRLS—NO JOB TONIGHT, I'M AFRAID. MY HUSBAND'S GONE DOWN WITH FLU, SO WE SHAN'T NEED A BABY-SITTER AFTER ALL.

SUZANNE and Sally Smith earned extra pocket money by doing odd jobs. They were known in their home town as "The Slave Girls"— because their gimmick was dressing up as Roman slaves!
One evening—

As the disappointed Slave Girls walked home—

LOOK AT ALL THOSE PEOPLE, SUZANNE. DON'T SAY WE'RE HAVING A POP CONCERT IN MARESBURY!

NEW CIVIC CENTRE

NO, SALLY. I SAW IT IN THE PAPER—IT'S THE RIVERA OPERA COMPANY, STARTING A TOUR. NOT EXACTLY OUR SCENE, IS IT?

IT'S AN OPERA ABOUT ANCIENT EGYPT.

RIVERA OPERA COMPANY
PRINCESS OF THE NILE

LOOK, THE CHEAPEST SEATS ARE ONLY 20P— LET'S GO IN, AND RISK FEELING LIKE MUMMIES BY THE END OF THE EVENING!

THERE'S MELISSA ANDERSON ARRIVING. TONIGHT IS HER FIRST LEADING ROLE.

SHE'S PRETTY—BUT SHE LOOKS TERRIBLY PALE.

Some minutes later—

AN AMBULANCE, SUZANNE! I WONDER WHO'S ILL?

AMBULANCE

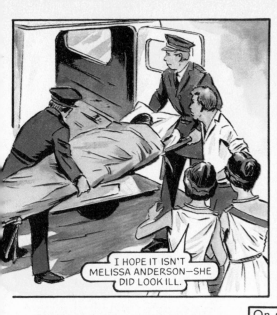

I HOPE IT ISN'T MELISSA ANDERSON—SHE DID LOOK ILL.

NO, IT ISN'T MELISSA. A STAGE-HAND COLLAPSED WITH A SEVERE ATTACK OF FLU—AND THAT MEANS WE'RE IN TROUBLE. WE'RE A SMALL TOURING COMPANY, AND EVERYBODY HAS PLENTY TO DO ALREADY.

SALLY! ARE YOU THINKING WHAT **I'M** THINKING?

WE CALL OURSELVES THE SLAVE GIRLS. WE DO ODD JOBS—AND WE'VE HAD BACKSTAGE EXPERIENCE!

WELL, YOU CAN CERTAINLY HELP US OUT TONIGHT.

On stage—

I'LL SHOW YOU WHERE THE SCENERY HAS TO GO FOR THE FIRST ACT.

YOU'RE CERTAINLY A PILLAR OF STRENGTH, SALLY—OR SHOULD I CALL YOU SAMSON?

NOW WE'RE MOVING THE PYRAMIDS, SUZANNE!

HURRY, GIRLS. IT'S NEARLY TIME FOR CURTAIN UP.

Backstage—

LISTEN, SALLY—I CAN HEAR SOMEONE CRYING.

THAT'S MELISSA ANDERSON'S DRESSING ROOM.

13

In spite of her doubts, Melissa Anderson sang magnificently.

The last scene—

But suddenly—

OH, NO! LOOK, SUZANNE— SHE'S FAINTING, AND IT'S NO ACT!

THIS WILL RUIN THE BEST SCENE!

The Slave Girls thought quickly.

GRAB SOME OF THOSE RUGS, SUZANNE—AND HURRY!

THANK GOODNESS WE'RE WEARING OUR SLAVE COSTUMES. EVERYONE WILL THINK WE'RE ACTORS.

WHAT A MARVELLOUS ENDING! MELISSA ANDERSON IS A MAGNIFICENT ACTRESS, AS WELL AS A FINE SINGER.

Later, in the dressing room—

I'M FEELING BETTER NOW. THANK GOODNESS YOU TWO WERE THERE!

I'M GLAD WE WERE ABLE TO SAVE YOUR WONDERFUL PERFORMANCE.

HERE ARE YOUR WAGES, SLAVE GIRLS—AND SOME TICKETS FOR THE NEXT SHOW HERE. I'M AFRAID IT'S ONLY A POP GROUP— SLADE, OR SOMETHING.

I THINK WE CAN PUT UP WITH THAT—CAN'T WE, SALLY?

THE END